Houghton Mifflin

ENJO

LITERACY ACTIVITY BOOK
Teacher's Annotated Edition

Senior Authors
J. David Cooper
John J. Pikulski

Authors
Kathryn H. Au
Margarita Calderón
Jacqueline C. Comas
Marjorie Y. Lipson
J. Sabrina Mims
Susan E. Page
Sheila W. Valencia
MaryEllen Vogt

Consultants
Dolores Malcolm
Tina Saldivar
Shane Templeton

INVITATIONS TO LITERACY

Houghton Mifflin Company • Boston
Atlanta • Dallas • Geneva, Illinois • Palo Alto • Princeton

Printed in the U.S.A.

ISBN: 0-395-72491-0

123456789-WC-99 98 97 96 95

CONTENTS

CONTENTS

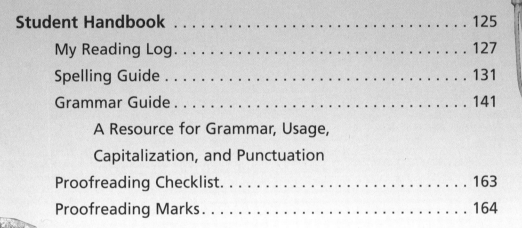

Illustration Credits
Susan Aiello 54, 78, 94, 108, 109; Elizabeth Allen 17, 29, 57, 81, 113; Shirley Beckes 114, 120; Ruth Brunke 66, 92, 97, 98, 106; Robert Burger/Deborah Wolfe 20, 83; Tony Caldwell/Cornell & McCarthy 61, 62; Estelle Carol/HK Portfolio 33; Olivia Cole/Asciutto Art Reps 74, 115; Ruta Daugavietis 7, 8, 70; Susanne Demarco/Asciutto Art Reps 13; Tom Duckworth 19, 24, 69, 71, 73, 82, 93, 95, 119, 122; Tom Durfee/Steven Edsey 11, 29, 38, 39; George Eisner/Steven Edsey 88; Bryan Friel/Steven Edsey 25; Dave Garbot 2, 9, 28, 35; Patrick Girouard 50, 80; Bob Lange 4, 67, 68, 75, 99, 102; Bert Mayse 12, 21, 49, 55, 59, 63, 79; Judith Moffatt 47, 51, 52, 57; Deborah Morse 32; Lynn Sweat/Cornell & McCarthy 26, 34; George Ulrich/HK Portfolio 46; Dave Winter 38, 118, 123.

Photo Credits
©Adamsmith Productions/H. Armstrong Roberts, Inc. 90; ©Alinari/Art Resource, NY 105; ©A.W. Ambler from National Audubon Society/Photo Researchers, Inc. 36, bottom left; ©Don Clark/Grant Heilman Photography 15, center left; ©Paul Dance/Tony Stone Images 47; ©Jack Dermid from National Audubon Society/Photo Researchers, Inc. 36, top right; ©H. Armstrong Roberts, Inc. 53, right; ©Hal Harrison/Grant Heilman Photography 36, top left; ©Grant Heilman Photography 15, center right, bottom; ©Breck P. Kent/Animals Animals 97; ©R. Kord/H. Armstrong Roberts, Inc. 53, left; Photograph ©1985 by Jill Krementz 116; ©Michael Newman/PhotoEdit 77; ©PhotoDisc 48, 52, 56, 60; ©Photo Researchers, Inc. 101; ©Alan Pitcairn/Grant Heilman Photography 22; ©Leonard Lee Rue III/Tony Stone Images 117, top right; ©Runk/Shoenberger from Grant Heilman Photography 36, bottom right; ©John Shannon from National Audubon Society/Photo Researchers, Inc. 15, top left; ©Jerome Wexler/Photo Researchers, Inc. 15, top right; All other photographs by Ralph J. Brunke Photography.

TO THE TEACHER

Welcome to the *Literacy Activity Book* for Invitations to Literacy.

In this book you will find a wealth of material to reinforce and enrich your students' learning in reading and the language arts. A variety of activities offer thematic and literature links, while providing in-context practice and application of what students are learning.

The pages in the *Literacy Activity Book* offer instructional support and practice in the following areas:

- ◆ Reading comprehension
- ◆ Word study
- ◆ Vocabulary
- ◆ Spelling
- ◆ Writing
- ◆ Grammar

In addition, pages for introducing and wrapping up the theme provide opportunities for meaningful thematic instruction.

Links to the literature provide context for learning.

Real-world formats enliven activities and familiarize students with types of writing they are likely to encounter as real-world readers.

Annotations in color help you evaluate students' work with ease. Pages where answers will vary offer good opportunities for discussion.

Graphic organizers help students clarify and organize their thinking.

Assessment tips suggest ways to evaluate students' work on appropriate pages. Other pages build background or help students plan their writing.

 Portfolio icons indicate pages that are suitable for student portfolios.

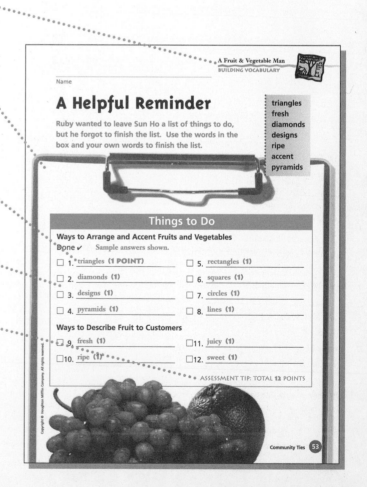

A Fruit & Vegetable Man
BUILDING VOCABULARY

Name

A Helpful Reminder

Ruby wanted to leave Sun Ho a list of things to do, but he forgot to finish the list. Use the words in the box and your own words to finish the list.

triangles
fresh
diamonds
designs
ripe
accent
pyramids

Things to Do

Ways to Arrange and Accent Fruits and Vegetables
Done ✔ Sample answers shown.

- ☐ 1. triangles **(1 POINT)**
- ☐ 2. diamonds **(1)**
- ☐ 3. designs **(1)**
- ☐ 4. pyramids **(1)**
- ☐ 5. rectangles **(1)**
- ☐ 6. squares **(1)**
- ☐ 7. circles **(1)**
- ☐ 8. lines **(1)**

Ways to Describe Fruit to Customers

- ☐ 9. fresh **(1)**
- ☐ 10. ripe **(1)**
- ☐ 11. juicy **(1)**
- ☐ 12. sweet **(1)**

ASSESSMENT TIP: TOTAL **12** POINTS

Community Ties **53**

READING

SELECTION CONNECTIONS pages help students consider the theme broadly, comparing and contrasting key elements of the selections.

Charts and graphic organizers provide easy-to-use formats that help students compare selections at a glance.

COMPREHENSION CHECK pages provide a variety of formats to help students demonstrate their understanding of what they have read.

COMPREHENSION SKILL pages reinforce students' understanding of the comprehension skill taught with the selection.

Labels indicate the selection name and its accompanying comprehension skill.

Directions establish a real-world context for the activity while guiding students through the page.

Writing opportunities encourage students to think critically about what they have read.

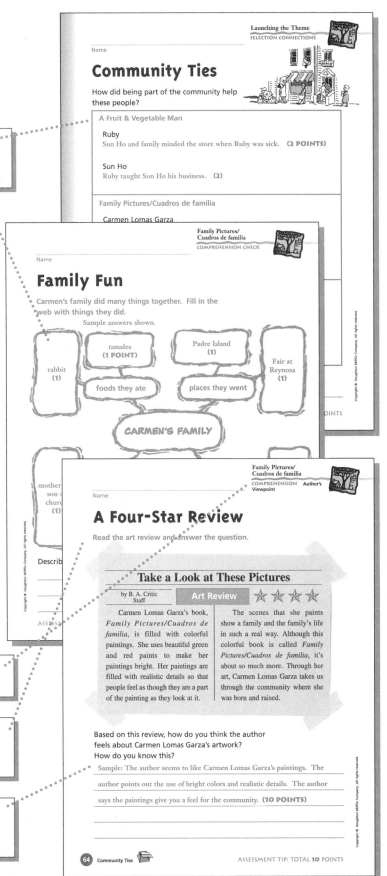

Launching the Theme
SELECTION CONNECTIONS

Name

Community Ties

How did being part of the community help these people?

A Fruit & Vegetable Man

Ruby
Sun Ho and family minded the store when Ruby was sick. **(2 POINTS)**

Sun Ho
Ruby taught Sun Ho his business. **(2)**

Family Pictures/Cuadros de familia
Carmen Lomas Garza

Family Pictures/
Cuadros de familia
COMPREHENSION CHECK

Name

Family Fun

Carmen's family did many things together. Fill in the web with things they did.

Sample answers shown.

- rabbit **(1)**
- tamales **(1 POINT)**
- foods they ate
- Padre Island **(1)**
- places they went
- Fair at Reynosa **(1)**

CARMEN'S FAMILY

mother son a church **(1)**

Describe

Family Pictures/
Cuadros de familia
COMPREHENSION Author's Viewpoint

Name

A Four-Star Review

Read the art review and answer the question.

Take a Look at These Pictures

by B. A. Critic
Staff   **Art Review**   ☆ ☆ ☆ ☆

Carmen Lomas Garza's book, *Family Pictures/Cuadros de familia*, is filled with colorful paintings. She uses beautiful green and red paints to make her paintings bright. Her paintings are filled with realistic details so that people feel as though they are a part of the painting as they look at it.

The scenes that she paints show a family and the family's life in such a real way. Although this colorful book is called *Family Pictures/Cuadros de familia*, it's about so much more. Through her art, Carmen Lomas Garza takes us through the community where she was born and raised.

Based on this review, how do you think the author feels about Carmen Lomas Garza's artwork? How do you know this?

Sample: The author seems to like Carmen Lomas Garza's paintings. The

author points out the use of bright colors and realistic details. The author

says the paintings give you a feel for the community. **(10 POINTS)**

ASSESSMENT TIP: TOTAL **10** POINTS

READING

WORD SKILLS pages enhance students' reading abilities by providing instruction and practice in analyzing word structure and understanding word families.

Lively formats pique interest and ground skill practice in selection content.

Practice items are individually scored for easy evaluation of student progress.

SELECTION VOCABULARY pages support reading comprehension by providing practice in key selection words.

BUILDING VOCABULARY pages extend students' word base by providing additional practice with key words and additional related words.

The word-box format clearly highlights selection vocabulary.

Activities provide practice based on reinforcing word meanings.

Additional related words enhance students' understanding of selection words and enrich their vocabulary.

Engaging formats motivate students to have fun with words and to use vocabulary in various contexts.

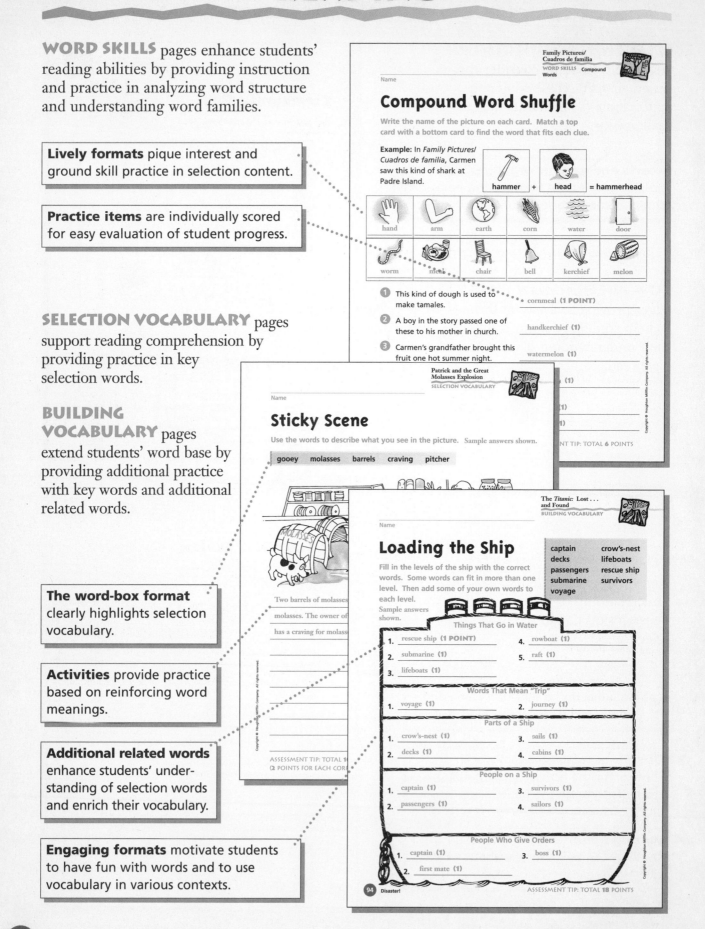

Family Pictures/
Cuadros de familia
WORD SKILLS Compound Words

Name _____

Compound Word Shuffle

Write the name of the picture on each card. Match a top card with a bottom card to find the word that fits each clue.

Example: In *Family Pictures/Cuadros de familia*, Carmen saw this kind of shark at Padre Island.

hammer + head = hammerhead

| hand | arm | earth | corn | water | door |

| worm | ... | chair | bell | kerchief | melon |

1. This kind of dough is used to make tamales.   cornmeal (**1 POINT**)

2. A boy in the story passed one of these to his mother in church.   handkerchief (1)

3. Carmen's grandfather brought this fruit one hot summer night.   watermelon (1)

Patrick and the Great
Molasses Explosion
SELECTION VOCABULARY

Name _____

Sticky Scene

Use the words to describe what you see in the picture. Sample answers shown.

gooey   molasses   barrels   craving   pitcher

Two barrels of molasses

molasses. The owner of

has a craving for molass

ASSESSMENT TIP: TOTAL 1
(2 POINTS FOR EACH COR

The *Titanic*: Lost . . .
and Found
BUILDING VOCABULARY

Name _____

Loading the Ship

Fill in the levels of the ship with the correct words. Some words can fit in more than one level. Then add some of your own words to each level.
Sample answers shown.

captain	crow's-nest
decks	lifeboats
passengers	rescue ship
submarine	survivors
voyage	

Things That Go in Water
1. rescue ship (**1 POINT**)   4. rowboat (1)
2. submarine (1)   5. raft (1)
3. lifeboats (1)

Words That Mean "Trip"
1. voyage (1)   2. journey (1)

Parts of a Ship
1. crow's-nest (1)   3. sails (1)
2. decks (1)   4. cabins (1)

People on a Ship
1. captain (1)   3. survivors (1)
2. passengers (1)   4. sailors (1)

People Who Give Orders
1. captain (1)   3. boss (1)
2. first mate (1)

94 Disaster!   ASSESSMENT TIP: TOTAL 18 POINTS

WRITING

WRITING SKILLS pages provide support for planning writing in a variety of formats, as well as in-context practice opportunities for specific writing skills.

Links to the Literature help students make meaningful connections between reading and writing.

Graphic organizers provide structure as students plan what they are going to write. A variety of graphic organizers are used to complement different writing formats.

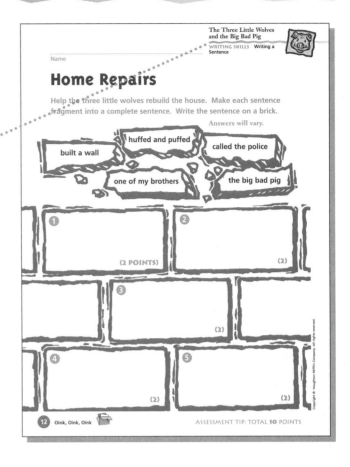

Practice activities provide real-world contexts and practical applications that help students vary and improve their writing style.

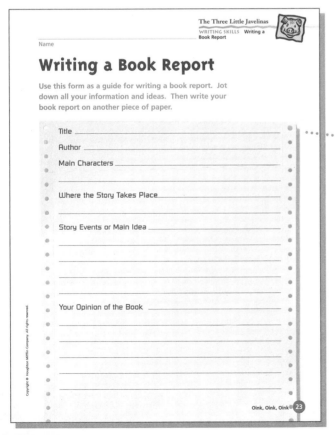

WRITING

READING-WRITING WORKSHOP pages support students during the important prewriting and revising stages of the writing process.

PREWRITING: CHOOSE A TOPIC pages help students answer the question *What can I write about?*

> **Topic ideas** stimulate students' thinking.

> Space is provided for students to write their own **personal topic ideas**.

> **Evaluation questions** help students narrow and choose their final topics.

PREWRITING: PLANNING pages focus on critical elements to think about *before* students write their drafts.

> **Graphic organizers** help students explore and plan their topics and ideas.

REVISING pages focus students' attention on the major characteristics of the writing form.

> A **Revising Checklist** helps students assess their first drafts.

> **Questions for a Writing Conference** focus discussion during peer conferences.

> **Graphic "notebook" pages** encourage students to make notes to remember ideas from their conferences.

A Special Day

Name

Do any of these ideas spark memories of your own?

A fun trip   An accident   Playing on a team   Moving to a new place

Ideas for My Story About Myself
Write three to five ideas for a story about yourself.

Think about each idea on your list.
Ask yourself these questions.

Can I remember this experience clearly?

Why do I want to write about it?

Circle the story idea you

Do You Remember?

Name

Close your eyes and picture your story.
Write notes that answ

Who else is in your story?

What happens?

Draw the most important part of your story in this circle. Make your picture as detailed as possible.

Making It Better

Name

◆ Revising Checklist ◆

Ask yourself these questions about your story.

- ❏ Does my story have a beginning, a middle, and an end?
- ❏ Does the beginning lead quickly into the main event?
- ❏ Do all my sentences keep to the topic?
- ❏ Did I use details so that my readers can picture what happened?

Questions for a Writing Conference
Use these questions to help you discuss your story with a classmate.

- What is best about this story?
- Does the story begin in an interesting way?
- Which parts do not keep to the topic?
- Which parts are hard to picture? What details are needed?
- How did the people feel? Are more details needed?

Write notes to help you remember the ideas from your writing conference.

My Notes

SPELLING

SPELLING pages support and extend spelling instruction. Spelling lists and spelling principles are presented in an easy-to-read format. Activities give students the opportunity to practice spelling in a meaningful context.

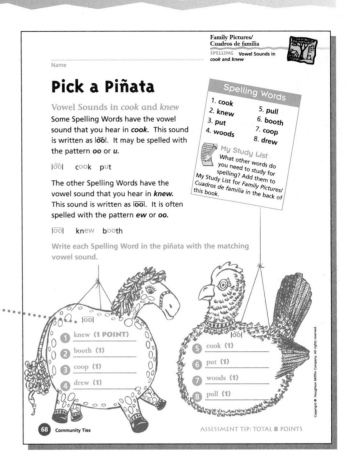

Family Pictures/
Cuadros de familia
SPELLING   Vowel Sounds in
cook and knew

Name

Pick a Piñata

Vowel Sounds in *cook* and *knew*

Some Spelling Words have the vowel sound that you hear in **cook.** This sound is written as |ŏŏ|. It may be spelled with the pattern *oo* or *u.*

|ŏŏ| c**oo**k   p**u**t

The other Spelling Words have the vowel sound that you hear in **knew.** This sound is written as |ōō|. It is often spelled with the pattern *ew* or *oo.*

|ōō| kn**ew**   b**oo**th

Write each Spelling Word in the piñata with the matching vowel sound.

Spelling Words
1. cook
2. knew
3. put
4. woods
5. pull
6. booth
7. coop
8. drew

My Study List
What other words do you need to study for spelling? Add them to My Study List for *Family Pictures/ Cuadros de familia* in the back of this book.

|ōō|
1 knew **(1 POINT)**
2 booth **(1)**
3 coop **(1)**
4 drew **(1)**

|ŏŏ|
5 cook **(1)**
6 put **(1)**
7 woods **(1)**
8 pull **(1)**

68 Community Ties

ASSESSMENT TIP: TOTAL **8** POINTS

> Students develop an understanding of spelling principles as they **sort** spelling words according to their patterns.

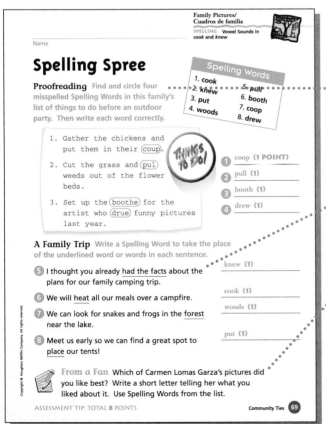

Family Pictures/
Cuadros de familia
SPELLING   Vowel Sounds in
cook and knew

Name

Spelling Spree

Proofreading   Find and circle four misspelled Spelling Words in this family's list of things to do before an outdoor party. Then write each word correctly.

Spelling Words
1. cook
2. knew
3. put
4. woods
5. pull
6. booth
7. coop
8. drew

THINGS TO DO!

1. Gather the chickens and put them in their (coup).
2. Cut the grass and (pul) weeds out of the flower beds.
3. Set up the (boothe) for the artist who (drue) funny pictures last year.

1 coop **(1 POINT)**
2 pull **(1)**
3 booth **(1)**
4 drew **(1)**

A Family Trip   Write a Spelling Word to take the place of the underlined word or words in each sentence.

5 I thought you already <u>had the facts</u> about the plans for our family camping trip.
knew **(1)**

6 We will <u>heat</u> all our meals over a campfire.
cook **(1)**

7 We can look for snakes and frogs in the <u>forest</u> near the lake.
woods **(1)**

8 Meet us early so we can find a great spot to <u>place</u> our tents!
put **(1)**

From a Fan   Which of Carmen Lomas Garza's pictures did you like best? Write a short letter telling her what you liked about it. Use Spelling Words from the list.

ASSESSMENT TIP: TOTAL **8** POINTS

Community Ties 69

> Practice in **proofreading** helps students develop their ability to identify and correct spelling errors in their own writing.

> Students use critical thinking skills to make the connection between **spelling and meaning**.

> **Writing applications** help students make spelling words a part of their reading-writing vocabulary.

GRAMMAR

GRAMMAR pages provide support for grammar, usage, and mechanics instruction that is tied to the literature. A variety of formats give students practical, meaning-based practice opportunities.

> Students are provided with **clear examples** of the grammar skill.

> Students explore language concepts in both **structured and open-ended activities**.

> Engaging practice activities give students an opportunity to **apply what they have learned**.

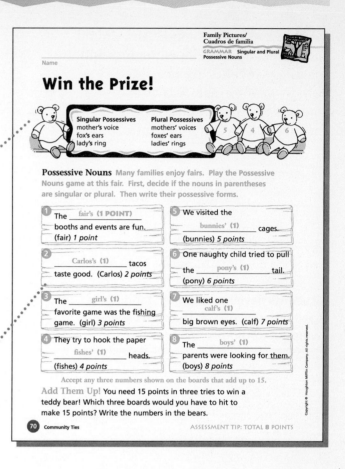

STUDENT HANDBOOK

A **STUDENT HANDBOOK** at the back of the *Literacy Activity Book* offers an easy-reference resource for support in reading; spelling; grammar, usage, and mechanics; and proofreading.

A **READING LOG** provides students with a place to record the books they read independently.

> A place for **Notes and Comments** encourages them to reflect on what they have read.

A **SPELLING GUIDE** gives students the support they need as they develop and practice their spelling.

> **Take-Home Word Lists** offer students a chance to practice the spelling words they have learned and to add their own words to their spelling lists.

> A list of **words from the literature selection** encourages students to increase their writing vocabularies.

MY READING LOG

Use this log to record the books or other materials you read on your own.

Date _____
Author _____
Title _____
Notes and Comments _____
_____
_____
_____
_____
_____

Date _____
Author _____
Title _____
Notes and Comments _____
_____
_____
_____
_____
_____

My Reading Log **127**

Spelling and Writing Word Lists

Name _____

✎ **My Study List**

1. _____
2. _____
3. _____
4. _____
5. _____
6. _____
7. _____
8. _____
9. _____
10. _____

• **Selection Vocabulary**

You may want to use these words in your own writing.

1. prowling
2. grunted
3. crumbled
4. trembling
5. scorched

How to Study a Word

LOOK at the word.
SAY the word.
THINK about the word.
WRITE the word.
CHECK the spelling.

134

Take-Home Word Lists

The Three Little Hawaiian Pigs and the Magic Shark

Spelling Long *a* and Long *e*
lāl	➔	shade
lāl	➔	tail, play
lēl	➔	beach, three

Spelling Words
1. three
2. tail
3. beach
4. play
5. deep
6. away
7. please
8. chain

Challenge Words
1. easy
2. really
3. reef
4. creature

My Study List ✎
Add your own spelling words on the back. ➔

133

Take-Home Word Lists

The Three Little Javelinas

Vowel-Consonant-*e*
lāl	➔	shade
lēl	➔	these
līl	➔	mice
lōl	➔	nose
lōōl or lyōōl	➔	use

Spelling Words
1. nose
2. these
3. shade
4. use
5. mice
6. smoke
7. snake
8. ripe

Challenge Words
1. escape
2. amaze
3. arrive
4. fortune

My Study List ✎
Add your own spelling words on the back. ➔

133

Take-Home Word Lists

The Three Little Wolves and the Big, Bad Pig

Short Vowels
lāl	➔	ask
lēl	➔	next
līl	➔	mix
lōl	➔	lock
lūl	➔	shut

Spelling Words
1. ask
2. next
3. mix
4. smell
5. black
6. shut
7. lock
8. truck

Challenge Words
1. knock
2. scent
3. plenty
4. fetch

My Study List ✎
Add your own spelling words on the back. ➔

133

STUDENT HANDBOOK

A **GRAMMAR GUIDE** serves as a quick reference to help students with their questions regarding grammar, usage, and mechanics. Students can use the guide as they draft, revise, or proofread their writing.

> Easy-to-understand **definitions** and **examples** help students understand basic language concepts.

A **PROOFREADING CHECKLIST** offers students a convenient, systematic way to check capitalization, punctuation, and spelling as they proofread their writing.

A chart of **PROOFREADING MARKS** gives students the tools they need to make changes and correct their work.

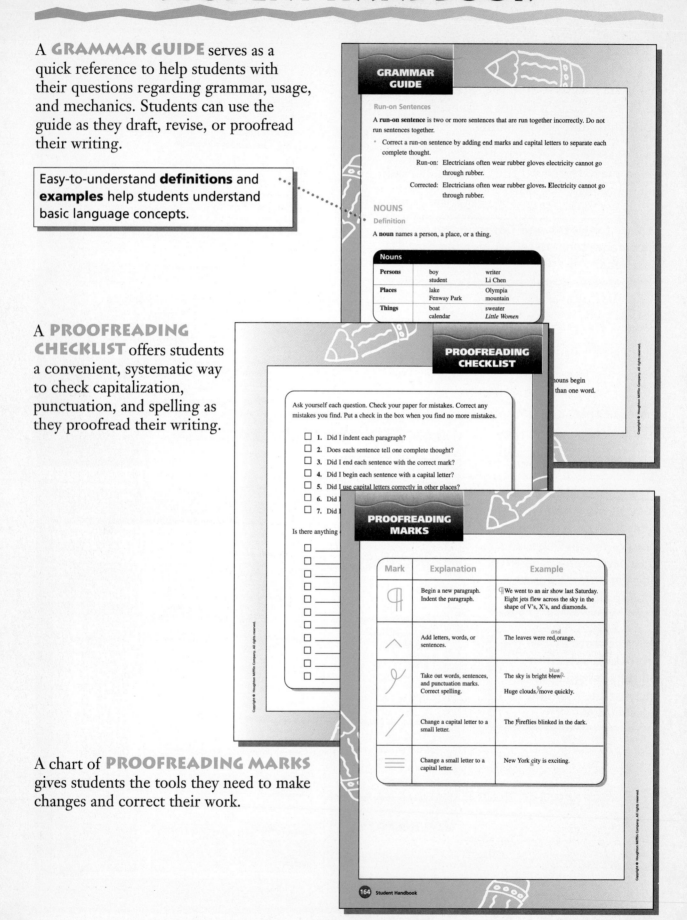

GRAMMAR GUIDE

Run-on Sentences

A **run-on sentence** is two or more sentences that are run together incorrectly. Do not run sentences together.

• Correct a run-on sentence by adding end marks and capital letters to separate each complete thought.

Run-on: Electricians often wear rubber gloves electricity cannot go through rubber.

Corrected: Electricians often wear rubber gloves. Electricity cannot go through rubber.

NOUNS

Definition

A **noun** names a person, a place, or a thing.

Nouns		
Persons	boy	writer
	student	Li Chen
Places	lake	Olympia
	Fenway Park	mountain
Things	boat	sweater
	calendar	*Little Women*

PROOFREADING CHECKLIST

Ask yourself each question. Check your paper for mistakes. Correct any mistakes you find. Put a check in the box when you find no more mistakes.

☐ **1.** Did I indent each paragraph?
☐ **2.** Does each sentence tell one complete thought?
☐ **3.** Did I end each sentence with the correct mark?
☐ **4.** Did I begin each sentence with a capital letter?
☐ **5.** Did I use capital letters correctly in other places?
☐ **6.** Did I
☐ **7.** Did I

Is there anything

☐ _____
☐ _____
☐ _____
☐ _____
☐ _____
☐ _____
☐ _____
☐ _____
☐ _____
☐ _____
☐ _____

PROOFREADING MARKS

Mark	Explanation	Example
¶	Begin a new paragraph. Indent the paragraph.	¶ We went to an air show last Saturday. Eight jets flew across the sky in the shape of V's, X's, and diamonds.
∧	Add letters, words, or sentences.	The leaves were red˄orange. (and)
⸋	Take out words, sentences, and punctuation marks. Correct spelling.	The sky is bright blew. (blue) Huge clouds move quickly.
/	Change a capital letter to a small letter.	The Fireflies blinked in the dark.
≡	Change a small letter to a capital letter.	New York city is exciting.

Name

My Reading Strategy Guide

As I read, do I **predict/infer** by . . .

Looking for important information? ☐

Looking at illustrations? ☐

Thinking about what I know? ☐

Thinking about what will happen next or
what I want to learn? ☐

As I read, do I **self-question** by . . .

Asking questions to answer for myself
as I go along? ☐

As I read, do I **think about words** by . . .

Figuring out words by using context, sounds,
and word parts? ☐

As I read, do I **monitor** by asking . . .

Does this make sense to me? ☐

Does it help me meet my purpose? ☐

Do I try fix-ups:

• Reread ☐

• Read ahead ☐

• Look at illustrations ☐

• Ask for help ☐

Do I **summarize**, both while I read and after reading by . . .

Thinking about story parts? ☐

Thinking about main ideas and important
details? ☐

As I read, do I **evaluate** by . . .

Asking myself how I feel about what I read? ☐

Asking myself if this could really happen? ☐

Name

Dear Friend

Imagine you are a teacher. Your class is full of students who behave very badly. One day a police detective visits your class. The students are horrible. Write a letter to your friend telling about the detective's visit to your class. Use each vocabulary word in your letter.

| misbehaving | detective | worst-behaved | change |
| act up | rapped | secret | |

ASSESSMENT TIP: TOTAL 10 POINTS (**1** POINT FOR USING EACH VOCABULARY WORD CORRECTLY; **3** POINTS FOR WRITING)

Name

Where Did She Go?

Complete the story map about *Miss Nelson Is Missing!*

Setting: Where did the story take place?

school

Main Characters: Who were the main characters?

Miss Nelson, students, Miss Viola Swamp

Problem: What was the big problem in the story?

Miss Nelson's class was very badly behaved, and she didn't know what to do.

Events: List at least three main things that happened.

Miss Nelson disappeared.

Miss Viola Swamp took her place and made the students work very hard.

The students searched for Miss Nelson but couldn't find her.

Ending: How did the story end?

Miss Nelson returned, and the students were good.

Name

The Writing Process

Prewriting
- Choose a topic.
- Plan your writing.

Drafting
- Write a first draft.
- Get your ideas down.
- Don't worry about mistakes.

Revising
- Read your draft thoughtfully.
- Make your ideas clear.
- Check the order.
- Think of strong words.

Proofreading
- Read your draft carefully again.
- Use proofreading marks.
- Correct spelling mistakes.
- Check capital letters and punctuation.

Publishing and Sharing
- Think of a good title.
- Make a clean copy and check it over.
- Find ways to share your writing.

Name

Off to a Good Start

Choosing a Topic List three or four choices to write about. Then put a check mark next to the one you will be writing about.

_____   _____

_____   _____

Plan Your Writing Write your topic in the top box. Put big ideas under your topic. Add details for each big idea. Keep adding ideas and details as you think of them. Use another piece of paper if you need more space.

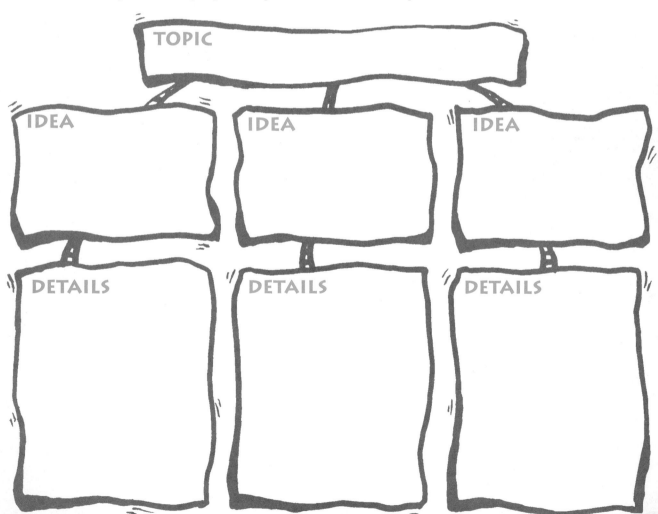

TOPIC

IDEA   IDEA   IDEA

DETAILS   DETAILS   DETAILS

Name

Revising Your Writing

Reread and revise your page of the class book. Use the
Revising Checklist as a guide. Then have a writing
conference with a classmate. Use the Questions
for a Writing Conference to help your partner.

● Revising Checklist ●

❑ Have I stated my main ideas
clearly?

❑ Are there enough details and
support?

❑ Is there anything I should leave
out?

❑ Are my ideas in a good order?

❑ Have I used interesting words?

Questions for a Writing Conference

- What is the best thing about this piece of writing?
- Does it stay on the topic?
- Does it seem well organized?
- Does it help me get to know this person?
- What additional information would a new friend like to have?
- Does it end in a strong way?

Write notes to help you
remember ideas from your
writing conference.

My Notes

_____

_____

_____

_____

_____

_____

_____

Name _____

Oink, Oink, Oink

Tale with a Twist Create your own fractured folktale. First, complete items 1–6. Then use those answers to complete the story.

1 Name a funny animal.

_____

2 Give the name of a faraway country.

_____

3 Name a food that you hate.

_____

4 Give a girl's name.

_____

5 Name an action verb in the past tense.

_____

6 Name an object you find inside.

_____

Once upon a time, there was a _____ family—
                                        1

a papa, a mama, and a baby. One day they went out for a walk in

_____ while their _____ cooled.
          2   3

Meanwhile, _____ entered their house. She ate
                      4

their _____. She tried all of their beds and then
            3

_____ on Baby's _____.
          5   6

When the _____ family returned, they found
                    1

_____ still asleep. When she heard them, she
          4

_____ again!
          5

Name

Oink, Oink, Oink

In Oink, Oink, Oink, you will read three funny versions of "The Three Little Pigs." After you read each story, fill in this chart.

Sample answers shown.

	The Three Little Wolves and the Big Bad Pig	The Three Little Javelinas	The Three Little Hawaiian Pigs and the Magic Shark
Setting	forest **(1 POINT)**	desert **(1)**	Hawaii **(1)**
Main Characters	pig three wolves **(2)**	Coyote three javelinas **(2)**	shark three pigs **(2)**
Building Materials	brick concrete barbed wire **(3)**	tumbleweed saguaro ribs adobe **(3)**	pili grass driftwood lava rock **(3)**
Main Events	Pig smashes down first two houses and uses dynamite on third. **(3)**	Coyote blows down first two houses. He tries to enter the adobe house through the stove pipe. **(3)**	When Shark's disguises fail, he blows down first two houses. He can't blow down the lava rock house. **(3)**
Ending	The wolves build a flower house and befriend the pig. **(1)**	The javelinas light a fire and scorch Coyote's tail. **(1)**	The shark blows himself out of air, and he's rolled up by the pigs. **(1)**

ASSESSMENT TIP: TOTAL **10** POINTS PER SELECTION

Name

Get the Message?

Detective Fox found these messages on his
telephone answering machine. Choose a word
from the box to complete each message.

crumbled	grunted	prowling
scorched	trembling	

Message #1

From: The Three Bears
We think someone has been

prowling **(2 POINTS)** around our
house. The porridge is gone, and
we found bits of bread

crumbled **(2)** all over the
floor. We're afraid to look in the
bedroom. Please come at once!

Message #2

From: Little Red Riding Hood
I'm at Grandmother's house.
I think there's a wolf in her bed,
and I'm _____ trembling **(2)**
with fear. Hurry! I'm really
scared!

Message #3

From: Mother Pig
My youngest son called yesterday.
His voice sounded strange. He

_____ grunted **(2)** _____ something
about a huffing and a puffing at
his door. Please check it out. His
house is the brick one.

Message #4

From: Little Red Hen
Someone turned the oven up and
burned my bread. It's absolutely

scorched **(2)** ! One of
those lazy animals must have
done it. There are tracks, so come
before it rains.

What a Week!

The Big Bad Pig wrote a letter to his brother.
Complete the letter to tell what happened in the story.

Name

Dear Hammond,

    I had an incredible week. It began when I came upon a

_____ brick house **(1 POINT)** _____ built by these three wolves. At first

I tried _____ huffing and puffing **(1)** _____, but then I decided to use a

sledgehammer to _____ knock it down **(1)** _____. Soon after, they

built a house of _____ concrete **(1)** _____. It was a bit more

work, but my _____ pneumatic drill **(1)** _____ smashed that house

down. Then they collected _____ barbed wire, iron bars, and armor plates **(1)**

_____ and built their strongest house. I needed

_____ dynamite **(1)** _____ to blow that one apart. Their

last house was the best, though. It was made of sweet-smelling

_____ flowers **(1)** _____. I decided this is where I'd love to

live! So now I play games like _____ pig-pong and piggy-in-the-middle **(1)**

_____ with my furry friends. Come visit sometime!

    Sincerely,

        _____ The Big Good Pig **(1)** _____

ASSESSMENT TIP: TOTAL **10** POINTS

Name

Winter Dance

Read the fable. Then complete the chart.

One winter day, some ants were hard at work in a field.
A grasshopper came along and asked if the ants could give him
a few grains of corn. "Please," said the grasshopper,
"for I am starving."

"What did you do all last summer while we
gathered food?" the ants asked.

The grasshopper replied, "I was busy singing."

"Then you can dance all winter," said the ants.

Setting	a field winter **(1 POINT)**
Characters	ants a grasshopper **(2)**
Problem	Grasshopper needs food. **(2)**
Events	Grasshopper asks ants for grains of corn; ants ask what the grasshopper did all summer while they worked; grasshopper says he sang. **(4)**
Ending	Ants tell the grasshopper to dance all winter; he gets no food. **(1)**

ASSESSMENT TIP: TOTAL **10** POINTS

Name

Home Repairs

Help the three little wolves rebuild the house. Make each sentence
fragment into a complete sentence. Write the sentence on a brick.

Answers will vary.

built a wall

huffed and puffed

called the police

one of my brothers

the big bad pig

1 (2 POINTS)

2 (2)

3 (2)

4 (2)

5 (2)

ASSESSMENT TIP: TOTAL **10** POINTS

Name

What a Gift

The three little wolves bought their new friend the pig a T-shirt.
Solve the puzzle to find out what was printed on the shirt.

Each word has a base word. Write the base word. Then write
each numbered letter on the T-shirt.

precooked c o o k **(1)**
              8 14

mislead l e a d **(1)**
         4   9

remover m o v e **(1)**
            7

unfolded f o l d **(1)**
             2 13

enjoy j o y **(1)**
       1

agreement a g r e e **(1)**
              6   11

unhappiness h a p p y **(1)**
                            5

weekly w e e k **(1)**
        15

lived l i v e **(1)**
       12

selfish s e l f **(1)**
                  3 10

j o l l y
1 2 3 4 5

g o o d   f e l l o w !
6 7 8 9   10 11 12 13 14 15

ASSESSMENT TIP: TOTAL **10** POINTS

Oink, Oink, Oink **13**

Name ....

A Bad Temper

The Big Good Pig is feeling like a
Big Bad Pig again because he is
having trouble with the sentences.
Help him feel good by completing
each sentence with the better of
the two words in parentheses.

1 The three little wolves looked soft and

_____cuddly__ **(1 POINT)**_____ (cuddly, messy).

2 In order to sneak up on the wolves, the Big Bad Pig

came _____prowling__ **(1)**_____ (running, prowling) **through**

the trees.

3 The Big Bad Pig _____grunted__ **(1)**_____ (grunted, swayed)

because he was big and bad.

4 When the wolves were scared, they began

_____trembling__ **(1)**_____ (trembling, playing).

5 Each time one of their houses _____crumbled__ **(1)**_____

(crumbled, fetched), **the wolves were**

_____determined__ **(1)**_____ (frightened, determined) **to build a**

better one.

6 A burnt _____scent__ **(1)**_____ (scent, ceiling) **of the**

wolves' tails could be smelled after they were

_____scorched__ **(1)**_____ (huffed, scorched).

Name

Flower Power

Short Vowels Each Spelling Word has a
short vowel sound. A short vowel sound is
usually spelled **a, e, i, o,** or **u** and is
followed by a consonant sound.

short *a*	lăl	ask	short *o*	lŏl	lock
short *e*	lĕl	next	short *u*	lŭl	shut
short *i*	lĭl	mix			

Write each Spelling Word next to the
flower that has the matching vowel sound.

Spelling Words

1. **ask**
2. **next**
3. **mix**
4. **smell**
5. **black**
6. **shut**
7. **lock**
8. **truck**

 My Study List
What other words do
you need to study for
spelling? Add them to
My Study List for *The Three
Little Wolves and the Big, Bad
Pig* in the back of this book.

lăl
1. ____ ask **(1 POINT)**
2. ____ black **(1)**

lĕl
3. ____ next **(1)**
4. ____ smell **(1)**

lĭl
5. ____ mix **(1)**

lŏl
6. ____ lock **(1)**

lŭl
7. ____ shut **(1)**
8. ____ truck **(1)**

ASSESSMENT TIP:
TOTAL **8** POINTS

Name _____

Spelling Spree

Proofreading Find and circle four misspelled Spelling Words in this song. Then write each word correctly.

The Piggy Jig

Whenever the sky is rainy and (blak,)
I (locke) all my cares away.
Then I shut my eyes and (smel) the flowers,
And find the (nixt) mud hole for play!

1 black **(1 POINT)** _____

2 lock **(1)** _____

3 smell **(1)** _____

4 next **(1)** _____

Riddles Write a Spelling Word to answer each riddle.

5 If you have a question, you do this. What is this?

ask **(1)** _____

7 This opens with a key. What is this?

lock **(1)** _____

9 Your nose can do this for you. What is this?

smell **(1)** _____

6 Before you bake a cake, you do this. What is this?

mix **(1)** _____

8 This has four wheels. What is this?

truck **(1)** _____

10 Your eyes do this when you fall asleep. What is this?

shut **(1)** _____

 Build It Up Imagine that you are going to build something. On a separate paper, write step-by-step directions for how to do it. Use Spelling Words from the list.

ASSESSMENT TIP: TOTAL **10** POINTS

Name

Piece It Together

Subjects and Predicates

Color red each puzzle piece that
has a subject. Color blue each
puzzle piece that has a predicate.
Then cut out and match the puzzle
pieces to make sentences.

SUBJECT	PREDICATE
The wolf	laid the bricks.

Color red (1)
this story

Color red (1)
the four animals

Color red (1 POINT)
many famous stories

Color blue (1)
is a very old one

Color red (1)
it

Color blue (1)
scares some small children

Color blue (1)
live happily ever after

Color blue (1)
read the story to children

Color red (1)
teachers

Color blue (1)
are about animals

On another piece of paper, write the sentences. Begin each
sentence with a capital letter. End each sentence with a period.

Name

Picture Perfect

Subjects and Predicates The little wolves took pictures of
their homes. Write a sentence about each one. Write the subject
in the Subject box. Write the predicate in the Predicate box.

Answers will vary.

Subject	Predicate
(1 POINT)	(1)
(1)	(1)
(1)	(1)
(1)	(1)

ASSESSMENT TIP: TOTAL **8** POINTS

Oink, Oink, Oink **19**

Name

Way to Go

Two javelinas received secret directions from their sister. To confuse Coyote, she used the underlined definitions in her directions rather than the words themselves. Fill in the blanks with the correct words.

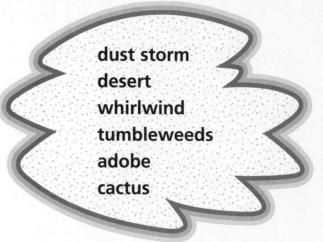

dust storm
desert
whirlwind
tumbleweeds
adobe
cactus

Walk a mile into our wonderful <u>sunny, sandy land</u> (_____ **desert (2 POINTS)** _____). Keep an eye out for you-know-who! If he does sneak up behind you, huff and puff to make a <u>blast of spinning air</u> (_____ **whirlwind (2)** _____) that will knock him right off his paws! Then RUN! Turn right at the <u>plant with the sharp needles</u> (_____ **cactus (2)** _____). Walk just a little farther. Look for some yellow flowers. It may be hard to see them since those <u>little rolling bushes</u> (_____ **tumbleweeds (2)** _____) are always getting in the way. I'll be in my cozy <u>mud brick</u> (_____ **adobe (2)** _____) house waiting.

WARNING: I heard there's a chance of a <u>sand and dirt twister</u> (_____ **dust storm (2)** _____). Come prepared just in case!

ASSESSMENT TIP: TOTAL **12** POINTS

Name

According to Coyote

If Coyote could talk, how would he tell the story? Complete Coyote's statements to retell *The Three Little Javelinas*.

1
The first javelina built a ___tumbleweed house **(2 POINTS)**___ _____ . I ___blew his house down **(2)**___ , but he got away!

2
The second javelina tried using ___saguaro ribs **(2)**___ _____ _____ . I knocked them down, but he and his brother ran away!

3
I pretended to be ___old and weak **(2)**___ _____ to get into the third javelina's house. When that failed, I tried ___to go through the stove pipe **(2)**___ _____ .

4
Ouch! The three javelinas surprised me by ___lighting a fire in the stove **(2)**___ _____ _____ . I'll never forget it!

ASSESSMENT TIP: TOTAL **12** POINTS

Oink, Oink, Oink **21**

Name

Like It or Not

How does the desert setting of *The Three Little Javelinas* compare and contrast with where you live? Think about the weather, the land, the plants, and the animals.

Write your responses in the Venn diagram. Remember that similar things in both settings go in the middle. Answers will vary.

ASSESSMENT TIP:
TOTAL **15** POINTS
(**5** POINTS FOR
EACH COMPLETED
SECTION)

Desert

Both Settings

My Home Region

Writing a Book Report

Use this form as a guide for writing a book report. Jot
down all your information and ideas. Then write your
book report on another piece of paper.

Title _____

Author _____

Main Characters _____

_____

Where the Story Takes Place _____

_____

Story Events or Main Idea _____

_____

_____

_____

_____

Your Opinion of the Book _____

_____

_____

_____

_____

Name _____

Which Ending?

Coyote is clever, but he can't read the words on the chalkboard. Fill in the chart to help him to see that each word is made from a base word plus the ending *-ed* or *-ing*.

	Base Word	-ed or -ing
scaring	scare	ing
flipped	flip	ed
1. sneaking	sneak **(1 POINT)**	ing **(1)**
2. thanked	thank **(1)**	ed **(1)**
3. chased	chase **(1)**	ed **(1)**
4. topping	top **(1)**	ing **(1)**
5. piling	pile **(1)**	ing **(1)**
6. jogged	jog **(1)**	ed **(1)**
7. giggling	giggle **(1)**	ing **(1)**
8. mixed	mix **(1)**	ed **(1)**
9. winning	win **(1)**	ing **(1)**
10. dared	dare **(1)**	ed **(1)**

ASSESSMENT TIP:
TOTAL **20** POINTS

Name

Word Families

Put the words in the correct category. Some words may go in more than one category. Then add words of your own.

desert	**dust storm**	**whirlwind**	**tumbleweeds**
cactus	**adobe**	**saguaro**	**palo verde**

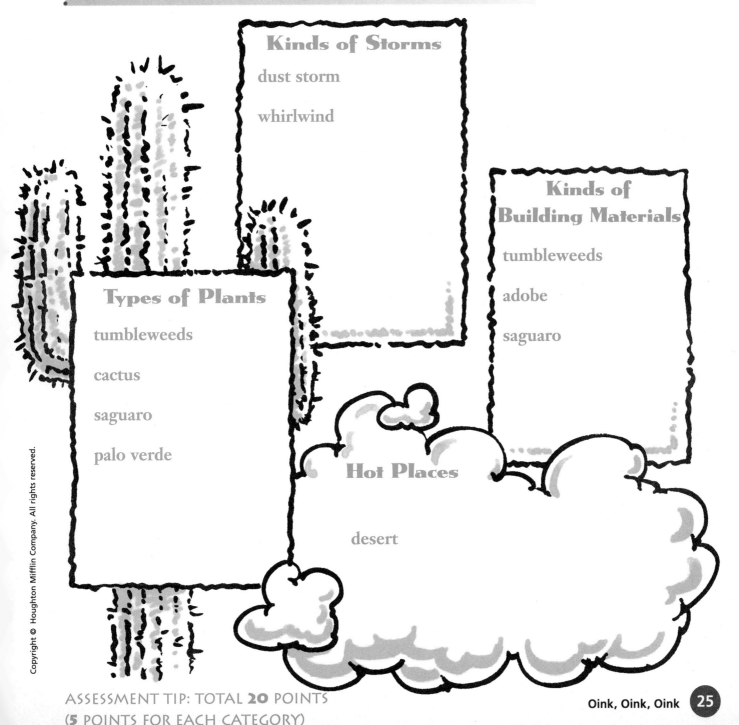

Kinds of Storms

dust storm

whirlwind

Kinds of Building Materials

tumbleweeds

adobe

saguaro

Types of Plants

tumbleweeds

cactus

saguaro

palo verde

Hot Places

desert

ASSESSMENT TIP: TOTAL **20** POINTS
(**5** POINTS FOR EACH CATEGORY)

Name

Home Sweet Home

Vowel-Consonant-e Each Spelling Word has a long vowel sound spelled with the vowel-consonant-**e** pattern.

long *a* |ā| shade
long *e* |ē| these
long *i* |ī| mice
long *o* |ō| nose
long *u* |yōō| use

Write the Spelling Word that matches the vowel-consonant-e pattern on each house.

Spelling Words

1. **nose**
2. **these**
3. **shade**
4. **use**
5. **mice**
6. **smoke**
7. **snake**
8. **ripe**

My Study List
What other words do you need to study for spelling? Add them to My Study List for *The Three Little Javelinas* in the back of this book.

|ā|

a-consonant-e

1. shade **(1 POINT)**
2. snake **(1)**

|ē|

e-consonant-e

3. these **(1)**

|ī|

i-consonant-e

4. mice **(1)**
5. ripe **(1)**

|ō|

o-consonant-e

6. nose **(1)**
7. smoke **(1)**

WELCOME

|ū|

u-consonant-e

8. use **(1)**

ASSESSMENT TIP: TOTAL **8** POINTS

Spelling Spree

Rhyme Time Write the Spelling Word that rhymes with the underlined word.

Spelling Words
1. nose
2. these
3. shade
4. use
5. mice
6. smoke
7. snake
8. ripe

1 The desert is hot. I'd love to <u>trade</u>

this sunny spot for some cool, dark _____shade **(1 POINT)**_____ .

2 "Oh!" cried the child, though the toy was <u>fake</u>.

It wiggled and slid like a long, black _____snake **(1)**_____ .

3 Ms. Glade sniffed the air and began to <u>choke</u>.

Wherever there's fire, there's usually _____smoke **(1)**_____ .

4 Ramon ate the pear without a <u>gripe</u>

because fruit is so tasty whenever it's _____ripe **(1)**_____ .

Proofreading Find and circle four misspelled Spelling Words in Coyote's diary. Then write each word correctly.

April 2
Poor me! I burned my (noes,) and I can't smell a thing! I can't run (thees) days either because I tried to (uze) my paws to put out the fire. Today, I'm starting a new diet! I'm just sitting here under a cactus, nibbling its ripe fruit, and dreaming about tasty (mise!)

5 ___nose **(1)**___

7 ___use **(1)**___

6 ___these **(1)**___

8 ___mice **(1)**___

See a Tree The javelinas lived among cactus and palo verde trees. On a separate piece of paper, describe a plant or tree where you live. Use Spelling Words from the list.

Name

Run-on Riddles

Run-on   This is the largest desert plant its fruit is red.

This is the largest desert plant.   Its fruit is red.

Correcting Run-on Sentences   Read each run-on sentence.
Then write the two sentences correctly. Last, answer the riddles!

ANSWERS?

1 She built a strong house it had a tin roof.

She built a strong house. It had a tin roof.

(1 POINT)

WHO WAS SHE?

third javelina **(1)**

2 He could make himself small he knew many tricks.

He could make himself small. He knew many tricks. **(1)**

WHO WAS HE?

Coyote **(1)**

3 He fell down his house fell down, too.

He fell down. His house fell down, too. **(1)**

second javelina **(1)**

4 Its fire did the trick Coyote was gone for good.

Its fire did the trick. Coyote was gone for good. **(1)**

wood stove or stove pipe **(1)**

5 They are made of mud people build with them.

They are made of mud. People build with them. **(1)**

adobe bricks **(1)**

ASSESSMENT TIP: TOTAL **10** POINTS

It's a Secret!

Correcting Run-on Sentences Find the secret word.
First, write the two sentences in each run-on sentence.
Write the first letter of each sentence in the box.

1 Two houses were very weak unsafe houses are dangerous.

| T | wo houses were very weak. **(1 POINT)** |
| U | nsafe houses are dangerous. **(1)** |

2 Mud bricks make a good house bricks last a long time.

| M | ud bricks make a good house. **(1)** |
| B | ricks last a long time. **(1)** |

3 Little stick houses give shade even these houses can be strong.

| L | ittle stick houses give shade. **(1)** |
| E | ven these houses can be strong. **(1)** |

4 Walls can be made of weeds every weed house needs support.

| W | alls can be made of weeds. **(1)** |
| E | very weed house needs support. **(1)** |

5 Each house was different desert houses are special

| E | ach house was different. **(1)** |
| D | esert houses are special. **(1)** |

Now write all the first letters in order to find the secret word!

| T | U | M | B | L | E | W | E | E | D |

ASSESSMENT TIP: TOTAL **10** POINTS

Oink, Oink, Oink   **29**

Name

Word Webs

Complete each word web.
Add one or two words from the box.

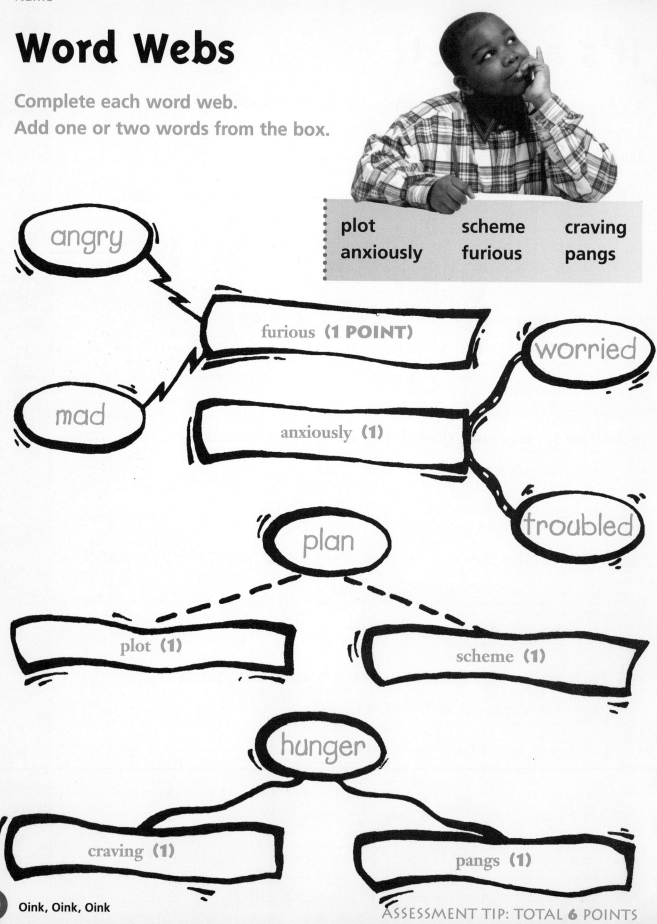

| plot | scheme | craving |
| anxiously | furious | pangs |

angry

furious **(1 POINT)**

mad

anxiously **(1)**

worried

troubled

plan

plot **(1)**

scheme **(1)**

hunger

craving **(1)**

pangs **(1)**

ASSESSMENT TIP: TOTAL **6** POINTS

Name

Hawaiian Style

Here are the
Hawaiian words
for *yes* and *no*.

yes = ae
(pronounced like
this: eye)

no = aole
(pronounced like
this: ah OH lay)

Read each sentence. If it tells something that happened
in the story, write **ae**. If it does not, write **aole**.

aole **(1)** ① The pigs' parents told them to watch out for wolves.

ae **(1)** ② The first pig built a house of pili grass.

aole **(1)** ③ The second pig built a house of seashells.

ae **(1)** ④ The third pig built a house of lava rock.

ae **(1)** ⑤ All three little pigs liked to fish.

aole **(1)** ⑥ One day the pigs caught a magic shark.

ae **(1)** ⑦ The shark blew down two of the pigs' houses.

ae **(1)** ⑧ The shark blew himself out of air at the third pig's house.

aole **(1)** ⑨ The pigs rolled the shark up and dumped him in the ocean.

ae **(1)** ⑩ The third pig helped his brothers build lava rock houses.

ASSESSMENT TIP: TOTAL **10** POINTS

Oink, Oink, Oink

Name

Is It Real?

Read the fable. Then write which parts are real and which are fantasy.

The Pig and the Sheep

One day a shepherd found a pig in his sheep pasture. He quickly caught the pig and tucked it under his arm. "I wonder what the butcher will give me for this fat little porker," he said as he started for town.

Now the pig started to squeal its head off — even though the shepherd wasn't really hurting it.

This puzzled the sheep, who followed and asked, "Why ever are you squealing so? *We* don't make such a fuss when he carries one of us off!"

Tearfully, the pig responded, "All he wants is your wool. But he wants my bacon!"

Moral: It's easy to be brave when your life is not in danger.

REAL

shepherd finding pig **(2 POINTS)**

shepherd talking **(2)**

pig squealing **(2)**

FANTASY

sheep talking **(2)**

pig crying and talking **(2)**

Two to One

This story is about the three little pigs and the magic shark. Look for five sentences that could be combined. Write them as compound sentences.

Three Little Heroes

This week, three little pigs have become heroes! They took care of a pesky shark. The shark came into their yard. The pigs ran inside to hide. One pig began closing windows. Another locked the front door. The shark started knocking with his big fin. He was very hungry. The pigs were very scared. The angry shark began to huff and puff. The house shook. Finally, the shark ran out of air. He fell in a heap. The pigs took him off to the dump. The shark won't be bothering them anymore!

Answers may vary.

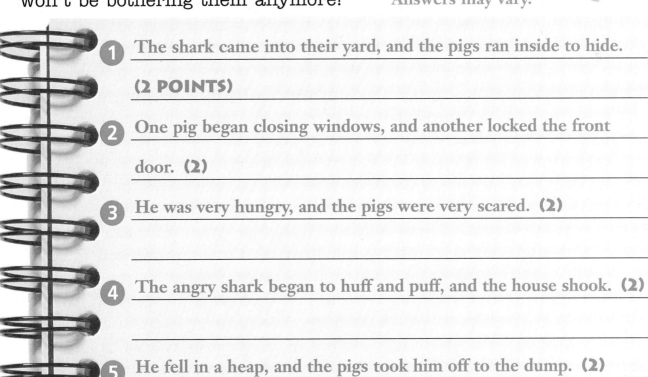

1. The shark came into their yard, and the pigs ran inside to hide. **(2 POINTS)**

2. One pig began closing windows, and another locked the front door. **(2)**

3. He was very hungry, and the pigs were very scared. **(2)**

4. The angry shark began to huff and puff, and the house shook. **(2)**

5. He fell in a heap, and the pigs took him off to the dump. **(2)**

ASSESSMENT TIP: TOTAL **10** POINTS

Oink, Oink, Oink **33**

Name

Figure It Out

Use context clues to figure out the meaning of each underlined word. Circle the clues in the sentence. Then write the meaning.

Answers may vary.

1 The mother and father warned the little pigs not to <u>squander</u> their money (but to spend it wisely.)

waste **(2 POINTS)**

2 The shark (wore a costume) to <u>deceive</u> the little pigs.

fool **(2)**

3 The (sharp teeth of the shark) filled the little pigs with <u>trepidation</u>.

fear **(2)**

4 The shark (blew so hard) that he (collapsed) like a <u>deflated</u> balloon.

with no air **(2)**

5 When the (shark) was (gone,) the <u>jubilant</u> pigs (laughed) with (joy.)

happy **(2)**

6 At the party, the pigs wore leis of (yellow, pink,) and <u>magenta</u> flowers.

a color **(2)**

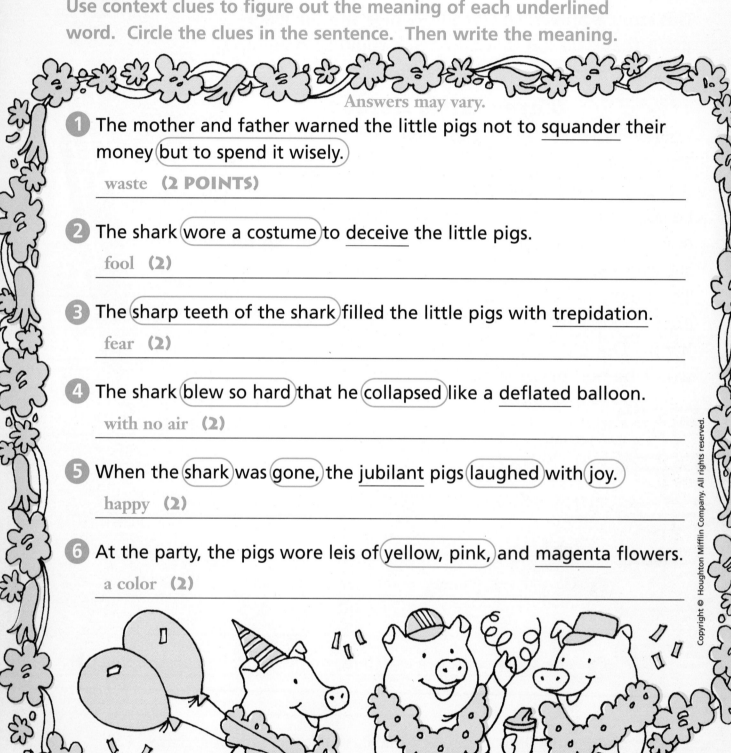

ASSESSMENT TIP: TOTAL **12** POINTS

Name

It's Puzzling!

Find the words from the box in the word search. Words can go across, up, down, or diagonally. When you have found all the words, answer the questions.

craving	furious
anxiously	sorrow
plot	sturdy
scheme	roared
pangs	firm

```
A N X M S C H E M E
G N R O E R I C P R
O I X B C P A N G S
F U R I O U S S U T
P E Z S O R R O W U
L C T I Y U N R J R
O W H O Q J S O M D
T U E A W E A L S Y
C R A V I N G Z Y E
A N X T R O A R E D
```

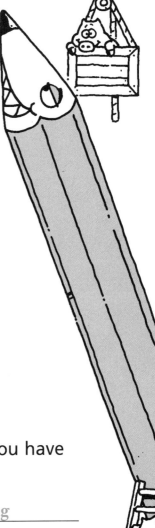

1 When you have hunger **pangs,** for what do you have a **craving**?

Sample: You probably have a craving for something

good to eat. **(1)**

2 What do people do when they **plot** and **scheme**?

Sample: They think of a plan to get what they want. **(1)**

ASSESSMENT TIP: TOTAL **12** POINTS
(**10** POINTS FOR THE PUZZLE AND **1** POINT FOR EACH QUESTION)

Name

Sea Sights

Long *a* and Long *e* Some Spelling Words have the |ā| sound spelled with the pattern *ai* or *ay*.

|ā| t**ai**l pl**ay**

The other Spelling Words have the |ē| sound spelled with the pattern *ea* or *ee*.

|ē| b**ea**ch thr**ee**

Write the Spelling Words that match the pattern next to each sea creature.

|ā| → ai

1 tail **(1 POINT)**

2 chain **(1)**

|ā| → ay

5 play **(1)**

6 away **(1)**

|ē| → ea

3 beach **(1)**

4 please **(1)**

|ē| → ee

7 three **(1)**

8 deep **(1)**

ASSESSMENT TIP: TOTAL **8** POINTS

Name

Spelling Spree

Hink Pinks Write the Spelling Word that fits the clue and rhymes with the given word.

Example:

a daring rescue   a brave <u>save</u>

1 twenty-four hours of games   a ___ play ___ **(1 POINT)** ___ day

2 an army car stuck in a huge hole   a ___ deep **(1)** ___ jeep

3 metal links that are not fancy   a plain ___ chain **(1)** ___

4 a white bird's end feathers   a pale ___ tail **(1)** ___

Proofreading Find and circle four misspelled Spelling Words in this invitation. Then write each word correctly.

5 please **(1)**
___

6 beach **(1)**
___

7 three **(1)**
___

8 away **(1)**
___

Dear Friend,

It would (pleaze) us to have you come to our (beech) party next Sunday. We will meet at (threa) o'clock at our house. We will swim, play games, and eat shave ice. Put (awai) all your work. Come have fun in the sun!

Aloha,

The Three Hawaiian Pigs

Party Time On a separate piece of paper, write an invitation to a party. Tell where and when it will be. Use Spelling Words from the list.

ASSESSMENT TIP: TOTAL **8** POINTS

Name _____

Asking or Telling

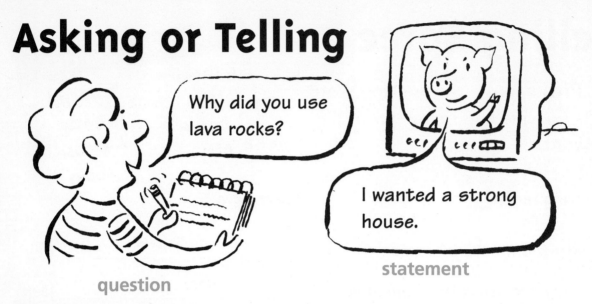

Why did you use lava rocks?

question

I wanted a strong house.

statement

Kinds of Sentences Jamie interviewed the third little pig. Three questions and answers are given below. Write each question and its answer on a notepad. Add the correct end marks.

> How long did you work on your house   I saw him in the water
> Where did you first see the shark   I was terrified
> I worked for a whole month   Were you afraid

Q. How long did you work on your house? **(2 POINTS)**

A. I worked for a whole month. **(2)**

Q. Where did you first see the shark? **(2)**

A. I saw him in the water. **(2)**

Q. Were you afraid? **(2)**

A. I was terrified. **(2)**

Extra! Interview the shark! Write your questions and his answers on another sheet of paper. Write at least two questions and two statements.

ASSESSMENT TIP: TOTAL **12** POINTS

Name

What Kind?

Go this way to the beach.

COMMAND

What a perfect day!

EXCLAMATION

Kinds of Sentences Help the Hawaiian pigs make some
signs for the beach. Each sentence is a command or an
exclamation. Add the correct end mark. Then write **command**
or **exclamation** to show what kind of sentence it is.

1 Rent a fishing boat.

command **(2 POINTS)**

2 Walk this way to the beach.

command **(2)**

3 Sharks swim here!

exclamation **(2)**

4 That is a shark!

exclamation **(2)**

5 Give me your hand.

command **(2)**

6 How hot it is!

exclamation **(2)**

Extra! Write a command and an exclamation of your own.
Use correct end marks. Label each sentence. Answers may vary.

7 _____ **(1)** _____ **(1)**

8 _____ **(1)** _____ **(1)**

ASSESSMENT TIP: TOTAL **16** POINTS

Name ....

Terrific Topics

Story Ideas Do any of these ideas spark an idea for your story?

- a strange friendship between a wolf and a pig
- a trip in a time machine
- taking a rocket to Jupiter
- finding a lost puppy
- an amazing amusement park
- a talking ant

My Story Ideas

Write five ideas for your own story here.

_____

_____

_____

_____

_____

Think about each idea you wrote. Then ask yourself the three questions.

Can I picture the characters and setting clearly?

Do I have enough ideas for the beginning, middle, and end?

Do I really want to write about this idea?

Name

A Good Start

Write and draw details about your story.
Use another piece of paper if you need more space.

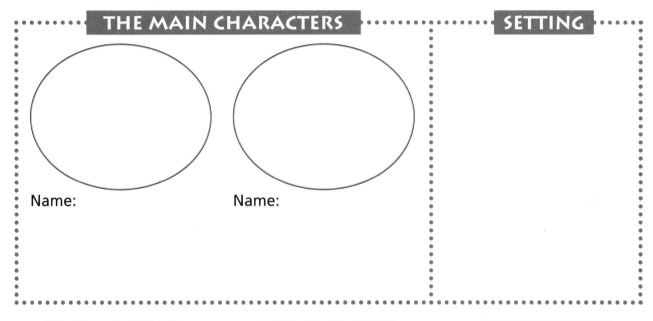

THE MAIN CHARACTERS

Name:

Name:

SETTING

BEGINNING

MIDDLE

END

Name

Take Another Look

• Revising Checklist •

Read your story to yourself. Ask yourself these questions and make changes.

❏ Does it have a beginning, a middle, and an end?

❏ Does it tell about one problem or situation?

❏ Did I use dialogue?

❏ Could my readers picture the characters and the events?

Questions for a Writing Conference

Use these questions to help you discuss your story with a classmate.

• Does the story begin in an interesting way?

• Are any parts not clear?

• Do any parts not belong in this story?

• Does the ending make sense? Can it be more interesting?

• What other ways might the story end?

Write notes to remember ideas.

My Notes

Name

New Pigs on the Block

Read this summary of "The Three Little Pigs."

    Three pigs built houses of straw, sticks, and bricks. A wolf blew down the straw and the stick houses and ate the two pigs. The wolf couldn't blow down the brick house, so he jumped down the chimney and fell into a pot of soup on the fire. Then the third pig ate the wolf.

Invent your own version of "The Three Little Pigs." Use the chart to help you. Check whether each part of your story is alike or different from "The Three Little Pigs."

	Alike	Different
Characters		
Problem		
Events 1. 2. 3.		
Ending		

On a strip of paper, draw your story scenes in order. Use your story strip to tell your version of "The Three Little Pigs."

Checklist   Use this list to check your work.

❏ My story retells "The Three Little Pigs" in a new way.

❏ My story has characters, a problem, events, and an ending.

❏ I can use my story strip to tell my story.

❏ I can compare my story to "The Three Little Pigs."

ASSESSMENT TIP: SEE RUBRIC ON
TEACHER'S BOOK P. 119A.

Oink, Oink, Oink 43

Name _____

Community Ties

Read the flyer and respond to the request for help.

SAVE YOUR COMMUNITY CENTER

We need your help to repair the community center. You can help by raising money or by hammering a nail. Please let us know the different ways you can help us rebuild your community center.

YOU CAN HELP TOO!

Answers will vary.

- -

1 _____

_____

2 _____

_____

3 _____

_____

4 _____

_____

5 _____

_____

Please return this flyer to:

Your Community Leader
100234 Community St.
Your Community, Your State 01234

Name

Community Ties

How did being part of the community help these people?

A Fruit & Vegetable Man

Ruby

Sun Ho and family minded the store when Ruby was sick.   **(2 POINTS)**

Sun Ho

Ruby taught Sun Ho his business.   **(2)**

Family Pictures/Cuadros de familia

Carmen Lomas Garza

Carmen enjoyed the fair, birthday party, and *Las Posadas* with community members.   **(2)**

Her Family

Family members had fun participating in the fair, cakewalk, birthday party, and *Las Posadas*.   **(2)**

When Jo Louis Won the Title

John Henry

The people in Harlem made him feel happy.   **(2)**

Jo Louis

Jo Louis' classmate made her feel good about her name.   **(2)**

How can *you* be a helpful community tie?

Answer will vary.   **(2)**

ASSESSMENT TIP: TOTAL **14** POINTS

Name

Play with Your Food

Follow the directions to create your own market.
You may want to work with a partner.

1. Cut out all the items on this page.
2. Arrange the fruit in the shape of a **triangle**. **(2 POINTS)**
3. Now arrange the fruit in the shape of a **diamond**. **(2)**
4. Next, arrange the fruit in the shape of a **pyramid**. **(2)**
5. Then arrange the fruit in **designs** of your choice. **(2)**
6. Use the vegetable to add an **accent** to your designs. **(2)**
7. Finally, make a sign for your **market**. **(2)**

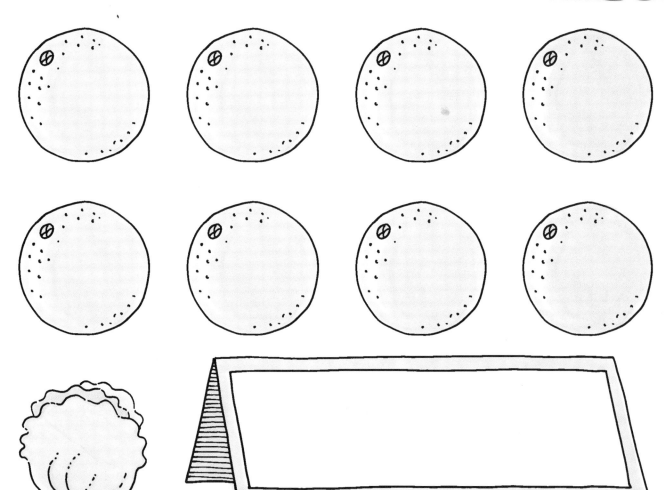

ASSESSMENT TIP: TOTAL **12** POINTS

Name

The Ruby and Sun Ho Story

Tell the story by filling in the chart.

Main Characters	1. Ruby 2. Sun Ho **(2 POINTS)**
Setting	Ruby's market in the city **(1)**
Problem	Ruby gets sick. **(1)**
Events	1. Ruby teaches Sun Ho how to run the store. 2. Trudy takes care of Ruby while he is sick. 3. Sun Ho's family takes care of the store while Ruby is sick. 4. Ruby realizes that Sun Ho's family can take care of the store. **(4)**
Ending	1. Ruby moves to the country. 2. Sun Ho's family takes over the store. **(2)**

ASSESSMENT TIP: TOTAL **10** POINTS

Name _____

Details, Details!

Look at the pictures. Write details from the story that tell
what is going on in each picture.

1

Ruby taught Sun Ho all about fruits

and vegetables. **(5 POINTS)**

_____

_____

_____

Sample answers shown.

2

Ruby arranged his fruit and vegetables

in many shapes, like diamonds and

triangles. **(5)**

_____

_____

2

3

People loved to go to Ruby's market

because he had the ripest fruit. **(5)**

_____

_____

ASSESSMENT TIP: TOTAL **15** POINTS

Writing an Essay

Think about the things that make you feel proud. Write down some of your ideas.

_____

_____

_____

Choose one idea that you might like to write about and circle it. Then write a sentence that expresses your feelings. Your sentence should answer this question: What makes me feel proud?

_____

_____

_____

Now list three or four examples of how this thing makes you feel proud.

_____

_____

_____

_____

Name

Market Day

Read about Ruby on the canopy. Find the plural nouns in the paragraph and write them on the base of the cart.

Ruby gets up at dawn every morning. He has to go to market to choose fruits and vegetables for his store. Ruby sniffs lemons, squeezes tomatoes, and wrinkles up his eyes to squint at the apples. He's on the lookout for bruises, worms, or rotten spots—only the finest for his customers back at the store! Ruby always teases his way to better prices while his purchases are weighed on the scale. Finally, he pays and makes his way back to his store in the city.

1. fruits **(1 POINT)**
2. vegetables **(1)**
3. lemons **(1)**
4. tomatoes **(1)**
5. eyes **(1)**
6. apples **(1)**
7. bruises **(1)**
8. worms **(1)**
9. spots **(1)**
10. customers **(1)**
11. prices **(1)**
12. purchases **(1)**

ASSESSMENT TIP: TOTAL **12** POINTS

Name _____

A Helpful Reminder

Ruby wanted to leave Sun Ho a list of things to do, but he forgot to finish the list. Use the words in the box and your own words to finish the list.

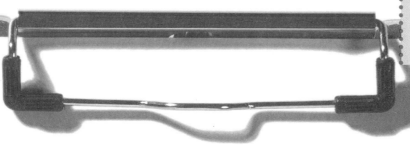

Things to Do

Ways to Arrange and Accent Fruits and Vegetables

Done ✔   Sample answers shown.

☐ 1. triangles **(1 POINT)**

☐ 2. diamonds **(1)**

☐ 3. designs **(1)**

☐ 4. pyramids **(1)**

☐ 5. rectangles **(1)**

☐ 6. squares **(1)**

☐ 7. circles **(1)**

☐ 8. lines **(1)**

Ways to Describe Fruit to Customers

☐ 9. fresh **(1)**

☐ 10. ripe **(1)**

☐ 11. juicy **(1)**

☐ 12. sweet **(1)**

ASSESSMENT TIP: TOTAL **12** POINTS

Name

Fruit Stand

Long *i* and Long *o* Some Spelling Words have the |ī| sound spelled with the pattern *igh* or *ie*.

|ī| r**igh**t   t**ie**

The other Spelling Words have the |ō| sound spelled with the pattern *oa* or *ow*.

|ō| s**oa**p   **ow**n

Help Ruby sort fruit. Write the Spelling Words that match the pattern with each kind of fruit.

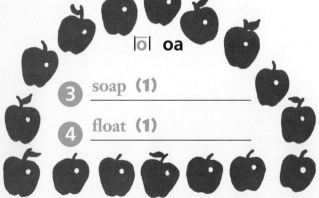

|ī| **igh**

1 right **(1 POINT)**

2 might **(1)**

|ī| **ie**

5 tie **(1)**

6 pie **(1)**

|ō| **oa**

3 soap **(1)**

4 float **(1)**

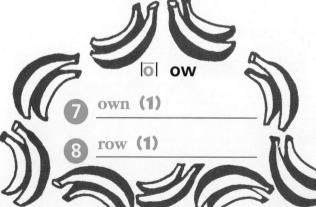

|ō| **ow**

7 own **(1)**

8 row **(1)**

ASSESSMENT TIP: TOTAL **8** POINTS

Name

Spelling Spree

Crossword Cart Fill the shopping cart.
Write the Spelling Word that fits each clue.

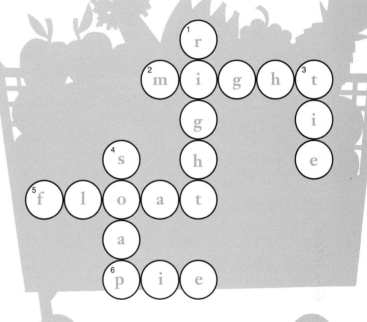

Spelling Words
1. own
2. right
3. row
4. might
5. tie
6. soap
7. pie
8. float

Across

2. may (1 POINT)
5. what boats do (1)
6. a dessert that may be
   filled with fruit (1)

Down

1. true or correct (1)
3. to knot laces together (1)
4. _____ and water (1)

Proofreading Find and circle
four misspelled Spelling Words in
this announcement. Then write
each word correctly.

Come to the Fruit Mart's first baking class! We use our (oan)
fruit to make your favorite (pye!) Choose from any (rowe) of apples,
peaches, or pears. Learn the (rite) way to make a crust. Then take
home what you make. You might be surprised at how good it is!

7 _own_ (1)   **8** _pie_ (1)   **9** _row_ (1)   **10** _right_ (1)

 Fresh Picks What is your favorite fruit or vegetable?
On a separate piece of paper, describe your choice and tell
why you like it. Use Spelling Words from the list.

Name

Boxes of Carrots

PEOPLE

child   children

PLACES

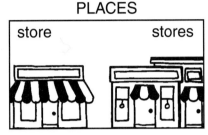

store   stores

THINGS

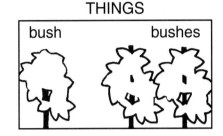

bush   bushes

Nouns Circle the nouns and write each one in a carrot.

1 The old (man) was like an (artist.) **(2 POINTS)**

2 Sometimes his (feet) hurt. **(1)**

3 The (children) loved the (store.) **(2)**

4 Some (berries) were piled in (boxes.) **(2)**

5 The (bunches) of (carrots) lay on a (shelf.) **(3)**

Draw two boxes on a different piece of paper. Cut and paste carrots with singular nouns in the box labeled **Singular**. Cut and paste carrots with plural nouns in the box labeled **Plural**.

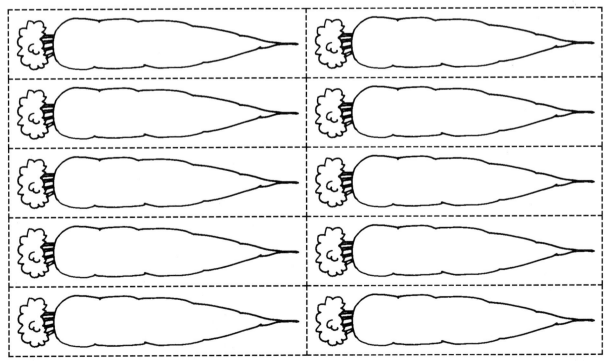

Name

A Letter to Ruby

Nouns

pear	pears	class	classes	penny	pennies	child	children
orange	oranges	bush	bushes	baby	babies	man	men
boy	boys	branch	branches	family	families	woman	women
		fox	foxes			mouse	mice
						tooth	teeth

Singular and Plural Nouns Help Sun Ho write a letter to Ruby. Write the plural form of each noun.

Dear Ruby,

I am very busy at the store. Every day I arrange the fruits

and _____**vegetables (1 POINT)**_____ . I put the _____**cherries (1)**_____ in
          vegetable   cherry

little _____**boxes (1)**_____ . Whole _____**families (1)**_____ come
          box   family

to buy _____**oranges (1)**_____ and _____**peaches (1)**_____ .
            orange   peach

Sometimes the _____**children (1)**_____ stay and watch me work.
                       child

I am doing some new things. We now sell _____**glasses (1)**_____ of
                                                    glass

fruit juice. We also have _____**dishes (1)**_____ of cooked vegetables.
                                  dish

All my _____**wishes (1)**_____ have come true! I hope that you
              wish

and Trudy are well.

Sincerely,

Sun Ho

Sun Ho

Name

Save It, Trade It

Complete and cut out the trading card. Draw a picture of
yourself on the back. Have fun trading with your classmates!   Answers may vary.

Name: _____ Age: _____

Favorite things to do: _____

_____

_____

When I write a book about my life, the first **scene** will be _____
(2.5 POINTS)

_____

_____

(2.5)

Someone who has **inspired** me is_____

because _____

_____

(2.5)

When I **recognize** someone I know, I_____

_____

(2.5)

A very important **custom** in my family is_____

_____

It is important because_____

_____

Name

Family Fun

Carmen's family did many things together. Fill in the web with things they did.

Sample answers shown.

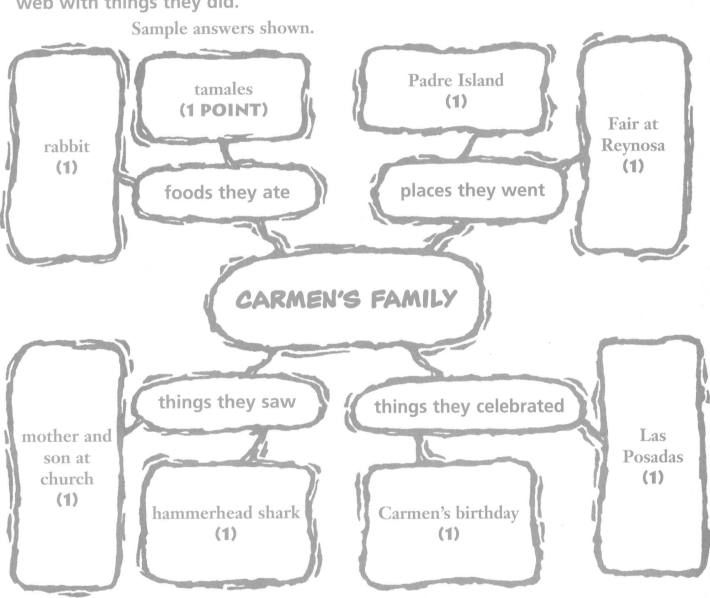

rabbit
(1)

tamales
(1 POINT)

foods they ate

Padre Island
(1)

places they went

Fair at
Reynosa
(1)

CARMEN'S FAMILY

mother and
son at
church
(1)

things they saw

hammerhead shark
(1)

things they celebrated

Carmen's birthday
(1)

Las
Posadas
(1)

Describe something that you do with your family.   Answers may vary.

_____

_____

(2)

_____

Name

A Four-Star Review

Read the art review and answer the question.

Take a Look at These Pictures

by B. A. Critic
Staff

Carmen Lomas Garza's book, *Family Pictures/Cuadros de familia*, is filled with colorful paintings. She uses beautiful green and red paints to make her paintings bright. Her paintings are filled with realistic details so that people feel as though they are a part of the painting as they look at it.

The scenes that she paints show a family and the family's life in such a real way. Although this colorful book is called *Family Pictures/Cuadros de familia*, it's about so much more. Through her art, Carmen Lomas Garza takes us through the community where she was born and raised.

Based on this review, how do you think the author feels about Carmen Lomas Garza's artwork? How do you know this?

Sample: The author seems to like Carmen Lomas Garza's paintings. The

author points out the use of bright colors and realistic details. The author

says the paintings give you a feel for the community. **(10 POINTS)**

_____

_____

ASSESSMENT TIP: TOTAL **10** POINTS

Name _____

A Journal of Your Own

Answer these questions. Then use the answers to start
your own journal.   Answers may vary.

1 Write about something you heard or saw this week
that made you laugh.

_____

_____

_____

2 Look around you. Do you see anything that is pretty or
unusual? Name the object and list a few words to describe it.

_____

_____

_____

3 Name a song you like. Write a few words about how
the song makes you feel.

_____

_____

_____

4 Name one thing you would like to do or see someday.

_____

_____

_____

....
Name

Compound Word Shuffle

Write the name of the picture on each card. Match a top
card with a bottom card to find the word that fits each clue.

Example: In *Family Pictures/*
Cuadros de familia, Carmen
saw this kind of shark at
Padre Island.

hammer + **head** = **hammerhead**

hand	arm	earth	corn	water	door
worm	meal	chair	bell	kerchief	melon

1 This kind of dough is used to
make tamales.   cornmeal **(1 POINT)**

2 A boy in the story passed one of
these to his mother in church.   handkerchief **(1)**

3 Carmen's grandfather brought this
fruit one hot summer night.   watermelon **(1)**

4 The fisherman at Padre Island may
have used one of these for bait.   earthworm **(1)**

5 This is a comfortable place to read
a book.   armchair **(1)**

6 You can ring this to be let inside.   doorbell **(1)**

ASSESSMENT TIP: TOTAL **6** POINTS

Where Did It Go?

Choose the word that best fits with each pair. Then find and circle all twelve words in the word search.

scene	inspired
custom	recognize

tradition   ritual

1 custom _____ **(1 POINT)**

know   remember

2 recognize _____ **(1)**

affected   caused

3 inspired _____ **(1)**

picture   setting

4 scene _____ **(1)**

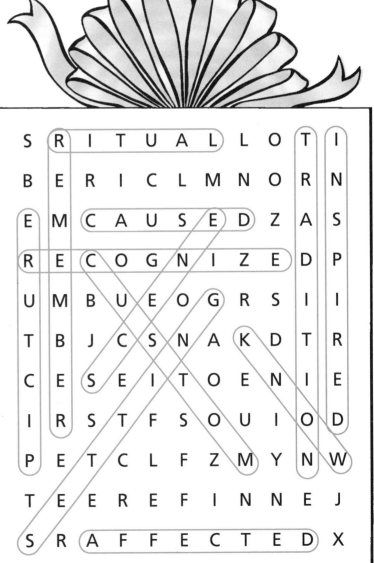

```
S  R  I  T  U  A  L  L  O  T  I
B  E  R  I  C  L  M  N  O  R  N
E  M  C  A  U  S  E  D  Z  A  S
R  E  C  O  G  N  I  Z  E  D  P
U  M  B  U  E  O  G  R  S  I  I
T  B  J  C  S  N  A  K  D  T  R
C  E  S  E  I  T  O  E  N  I  E
I  R  S  T  F  S  O  U  I  O  D
P  E  T  C  L  F  Z  M  Y  N  W
T  E  E  R  E  F  I  N  N  E  J
S  R  A  F  F  E  C  T  E  D  X
```

**ASSESSMENT TIP: TOTAL 16 POINTS
(1 POINT PER NUMBERED ITEM AND
1 POINT PER WORD IN WORD SEARCH)**

Name _____

Pick a Piñata

Vowel Sounds in *cook* and *knew*

Some Spelling Words have the vowel
sound that you hear in **cook.** This sound
is written as |ŏŏ|. It may be spelled with
the pattern **oo** or **u.**

|ŏŏ| c**oo**k   p**u**t

The other Spelling Words have the
vowel sound that you hear in **knew.**
This sound is written as |ōō|. It is often
spelled with the pattern **ew** or **oo.**

|ōō| kn**ew**   b**oo**th

Write each Spelling Word in the piñata with the matching
vowel sound.

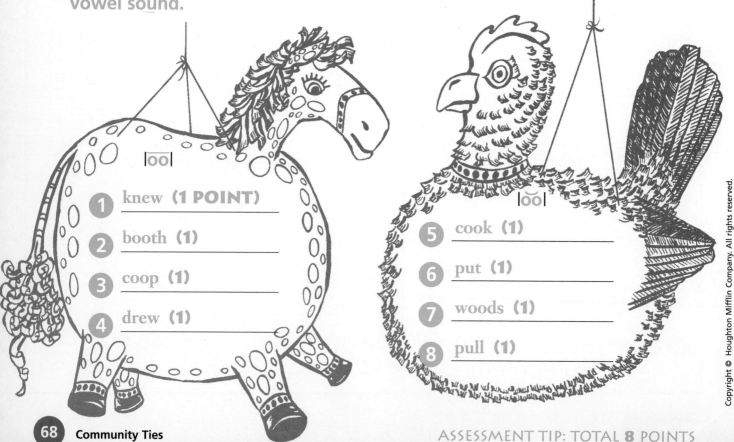

|ōō|

1 knew **(1 POINT)** _____

2 booth **(1)** _____

3 coop **(1)** _____

4 drew **(1)** _____

|ŏŏ|

5 cook **(1)** _____

6 put **(1)** _____

7 woods **(1)** _____

8 pull **(1)** _____

ASSESSMENT TIP: TOTAL **8** POINTS

Name

Spelling Spree

Proofreading Find and circle four
misspelled Spelling Words in this family's
list of things to do before an outdoor
party. Then write each word correctly.

Spelling Words

1. cook   5. pull
2. knew   6. booth
3. put   7. coop
4. woods   8. drew

1. Gather the chickens and
   put them in their (coup).

2. Cut the grass and (pul)
   weeds out of the flower
   beds.

3. Set up the (boothe) for the
   artist who (drue) funny pictures
   last year.

THINGS TO DO!

1 coop **(1 POINT)**
_____

2 pull **(1)**
_____

3 booth **(1)**
_____

4 drew **(1)**
_____

A Family Trip Write a Spelling Word to take the place
of the underlined word or words in each sentence.

5 I thought you already <u>had the facts</u> about the
plans for our family camping trip.

knew **(1)**
_____

6 We will <u>heat</u> all our meals over a campfire.

cook **(1)**
_____

7 We can look for snakes and frogs in the <u>forest</u>
near the lake.

woods **(1)**
_____

8 Meet us early so we can find a great spot to
<u>place</u> our tents!

put **(1)**
_____

From a Fan Which of Carmen Lomas Garza's pictures did
you like best? Write a short letter telling her what you
liked about it. Use Spelling Words from the list.

ASSESSMENT TIP: TOTAL **8** POINTS

Community Ties 69

Name

Win the Prize!

Singular Possessives	Plural Possessives
mother's voice	mothers' voices
fox's ears	foxes' ears
lady's ring	ladies' rings

Possessive Nouns Many families enjoy fairs. Play the Possessive Nouns game at this fair. First, decide if the nouns in parentheses are singular or plural. Then write their possessive forms.

1 The _____fair's (1 POINT)_____ booths and events are fun. (fair) *1 point*

2 _____Carlos's (1)_____ tacos taste good. (Carlos) *2 points*

3 The _____girl's (1)_____ favorite game was the fishing game. (girl) *3 points*

4 They try to hook the paper _____fishes' (1)_____ heads. (fishes) *4 points*

5 We visited the _____bunnies' (1)_____ cages. (bunnies) *5 points*

6 One naughty child tried to pull the _____pony's (1)_____ tail. (pony) *6 points*

7 We liked one _____calf's (1)_____ big brown eyes. (calf) *7 points*

8 The _____boys' (1)_____ parents were looking for them. (boys) *8 points*

Accept any three numbers shown on the boards that add up to 15.

Add Them Up! You need 15 points in three tries to win a teddy bear! Which three boards would you have to hit to make 15 points? Write the numbers in the bears.

ASSESSMENT TIP: TOTAL **8** POINTS

Name

Family Photo Album

Possessive Nouns Write a sentence to tell about each
picture in this family album. Make the noun beside each
picture possessive, and use it in your sentence.   Sample answers shown.

puppies

baby

Nat

Felix

Elissa

Grandmother

1 This huge bone was the puppies'
first gift. **(2 POINTS)**

2 The baby's sunglasses were a big
hit! **(2)**

3 Nat's new bike was purple and
silver. **(2)**

4 This is Felix's favorite spot. **(2)**

5 Elissa's costume won first prize.
(2)

6 Everyone wanted a ride in
Grandmother's new sports car. **(2)**

Name

Curious Questions

Fill in the survey by checking the two words that have
nearly the same meaning. Then answer the questions.

1 ☑ title fight   ☑ championship   ☐ practice   **(1 POINT)**

2 Describe how you might feel if you won a **title fight**.

Answers will vary.   **(2)**

_____

_____

3 ☑ yelled   ☐ whispered   ☑ bellowed **(1)**

4 When have you **bellowed** when you should not have?

(2)

_____

5 ☑ eased   ☐ braced   ☑ relaxed   **(1)**

6 Describe a time when you **braced** yourself.

(2)

_____

_____

7 ☐ unknown   ☑ name   ☑ title   **(1)**

8 Do you have a favorite **title?** What is it?

(2)

_____

9 ☐ tattered   ☑ new   ☑ unused   **(1)**

10 Would the President wear **tattered** clothes? Why or why not?

(2)

_____

_____

11 ☑ whirl   ☐ stop   ☑ spin   **(1)**

12 How would you feel after you **whirled** around a room?

(2)

_____

Name

What's It About?

Complete the summary for the book jacket for
When Jo Louis Won the Title.

When Jo Louis Won the Title

Jo Louis is worried about going to a new school

because _____

she doesn't want to tell people her name. **(2 POINTS)**

To help her, John Henry _____

tells her a story about the night he came to Harlem. **(2)**

When John Henry first got to Harlem, _____

he heard blues music. **(2)**

People were celebrating because _____

Joe Louis had just won the title fight. **(2)**

That night was special to John Henry because _____

Joe Louis won and because he met his future wife. **(2)**

Jo Louis is still a little scared when she goes to school.

But on that first day, _____

she meets Lester, and he tells her that she has a great name. **(2)**

ASSESSMENT TIP: TOTAL **12** POINTS

Name

Get in the Ring

Look at the pictures and answer the questions. Sample answers shown.

1 What general statement can you make about a boxer's typical day?

Boxers must do many kinds of

training to do well.   **(5 POINTS)**

_____

_____

_____

2 What general statement can you make about boxing rings?

All boxing rings are square, and

they always have ropes around

their edges.   **(5)**

_____

_____

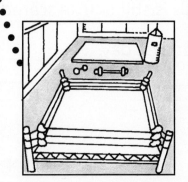

ASSESSMENT TIP: TOTAL **10** POINTS

Name

What's the Story?

Read the story about how this puppy got her name. Find
the five pairs of sentences that have the same predicates.
Combine the sentences in each pair by making a
compound subject with the word *and*. Write the new
sentences on the lines below.

My dog is named
"Shoe." Her name has a
story. My brother really
wanted a puppy. I really
wanted a puppy. My
parents said, "No way!"
My brother begged them.
I begged them. We
finally convinced them.

    We brought the
puppy home. My family
ate dinner. The puppy
ate dinner. She ate from

a little bowl under the table.
Suddenly, we heard growling. My
brother looked down. I looked
down. The puppy was chewing a
hole in Dad's shoe! Dad looked
mad. Mom looked mad. In one
week, our new puppy ruined seven
perfectly good shoes!

    Dad started calling her "Shoe."
It may seem like a weird name for
a dog, but like a shoe, it just
seemed to fit!

1 My brother and I really wanted a puppy. **(2 POINTS)**

2 My brother and I begged them. **(2)**

3 My family and the puppy ate dinner. **(2)**

4 My brother and I looked down. **(2)**

5 Dad and Mom looked mad. **(2)**

ASSESSMENT TIP: TOTAL **10** POINTS

 Community Ties 75

Name

Contraction Puzzle

Jo Louis learned something important from her grandfather. Solve the puzzle to find out what she learned. Write the two words that each contraction is made from. Then write each numbered letter on the line with the matching number below.

1 we're   w e __ a r e **(1 POINT)**
                    13 4

2 doesn't   d o e s __ n o t **(1)**
                         9

3 you're   y o u __ a r e **(1)**
                5   17

4 I've   I __ h a v e **(1)**
                   11 2

5 mustn't   m u s t __ n o t **(1)**
                8   14

6 she's   s h e __ i s **(1)**
                   1   12

7 needn't   n e e d __ n o t **(1)**
                6   16

8 they've   t h e y __ h a v e **(1)**
                      3   10 7

9 couldn't   c o u l d __ n o t **(1)**
                                   15

10 you'll   y o u __ w i l l **(1)**
                18

What Jo Louis learned from her grandfather:

E v e r y __ n a m e
1 2 3 4 5   6 7 8 9

h a s __ a __ s t o r y .
10 11 12   13   14 15 16 17 18

ASSESSMENT TIP: TOTAL **10** POINTS

Name

All Crossed Up

Complete the puzzle with words from the box.

| whirled | title fight | title | tattered | bellowed |
| braced | jazz | Harlem | daydream | perched |

Across

2. A hope or a wish **(1 POINT)**

4. The winner of this is a top boxer **(1)**

7. A popular American form of music **(1)**

8. Another name for *name* **(1)**

9. Yelled loudly **(1)**

Down

1. Sat atop **(1)**

3. Spun around **(1)**

5. Torn and ragged **(1)**

6. A famous part of New York City **(1)**

9. Prepared for something bad **(1)**

Moving Day

Vowel Sounds in *town* and *boy*

Some Spelling Words have the vowel
sound that you hear in **town.** This sound
is written as |oul. It is often spelled with
the pattern **ow** or **ou.**

|oul   t**ow**n   pr**ou**d

The other Spelling Words have the
vowel sound that you hear in **boy.**
This sound is written as |oil. It is spelled
with the pattern **oi** or **oy.**

|oil   n**oi**se   b**oy**

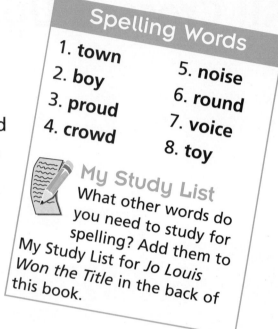

Spelling Words

1. town
2. boy
3. proud
4. crowd
5. noise
6. round
7. voice
8. toy

My Study List
What other words do
you need to study for
spelling? Add them to
My Study List for Jo Louis
Won the Title in the back of
this book.

Write each Spelling Word on the suitcase that has the
matching sound and spelling pattern.

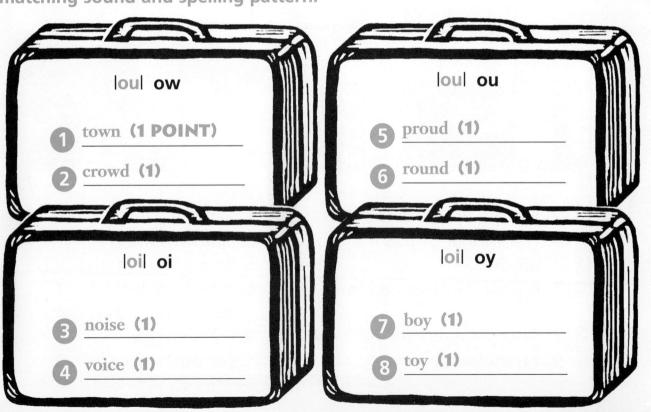

|oul **ow**

1. town **(1 POINT)**
2. crowd **(1)**

|oul **ou**

5. proud **(1)**
6. round **(1)**

|oil **oi**

3. noise **(1)**
4. voice **(1)**

|oil **oy**

7. boy **(1)**
8. toy **(1)**

ASSESSMENT TIP: TOTAL **8** POINTS

Name

Spelling Spree

A Proud Title Write a Spelling Word to
fit each clue.

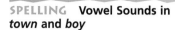

1 a large group of people

c   r   o   [w]   d **(1 POINT)**

2 what you use to speak   v   o   [i]   c   e **(1)**

3 a place smaller than a city   t   o   w   [n] **(1)**

4 the shape of a circle   r   o   u   [n]   d **(1)**

5 a sound   n   o   i   s   [e] **(1)**

6 pleased with oneself   p   [r]   o   u   d **(1)**

What word describes the boxer Joe Louis?
To find out, write the boxed letters in order.

w   i   n   n   e   r

Proofreading Find and circle four misspelled Spelling
Words in this post card. Then write each word correctly.

Dear Etta,
When are you coming to town? I want to show
you my new school. Today I met a nice (bouy) who
liked my name and my singing (vois.) You'd be
(prowd) of me—I shared my new (toi) with him!
  Love,   J. L.

7 ___boy___ **(1)**

8 ___voice___ **(1)**

9 ___proud___ **(1)**

10 ___toy___ **(1)**

Name Me If you could choose a new name for yourself,
what would it be? On a separate piece of paper, explain
your choice. Use Spelling Words from the list.

Name

Window Words

Common and Proper Nouns Find the nouns in each sentence. Write the proper nouns in the windows on the left. Write the common nouns in the windows on the right. Remember to use capital letters with proper nouns.

proper nouns	Nouns	common nouns
Jo Louis		girl
Chicago		city
Friday		day

The writer, ms. rochelle, wrote about new york city.

proper nouns	common nouns
1. Ms. Rochelle **(1 POINT)**	3. writer **(1)**
2. New York City **(1)**	

The neighborhood called harlem was named for a town in holland.

proper nouns	common nouns
4. Harlem **(1)**	6. neighborhood **(1)**
5. Holland **(1)**	7. town **(1)**

Many cars cross the bridges over the hudson river.

proper nouns	common nouns
8. Hudson River **(1)**	9. cars **(1)**
	10. bridges **(1)**

ASSESSMENT TIP: TOTAL **10** POINTS

Name

Trying Tongue Twisters Together

Common and Proper Nouns Jo and John Henry
are trying tongue twisters. Write each tongue twister
correctly. Begin each proper noun with a capital letter.

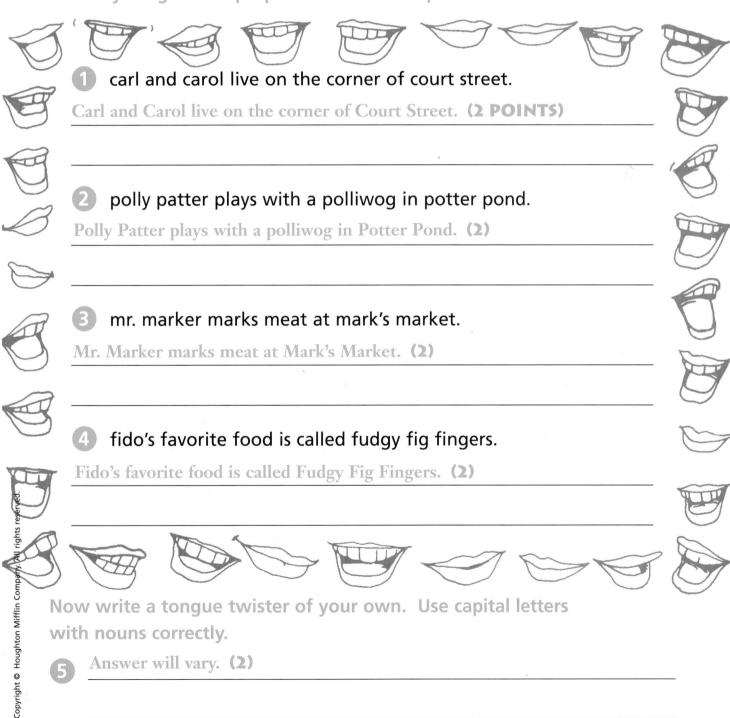

1 carl and carol live on the corner of court street.

Carl and Carol live on the corner of Court Street. **(2 POINTS)**

2 polly patter plays with a polliwog in potter pond.

Polly Patter plays with a polliwog in Potter Pond. **(2)**

3 mr. marker marks meat at mark's market.

Mr. Marker marks meat at Mark's Market. **(2)**

4 fido's favorite food is called fudgy fig fingers.

Fido's favorite food is called Fudgy Fig Fingers. **(2)**

Now write a tongue twister of your own. Use capital letters
with nouns correctly.

5 Answer will vary. **(2)**

ASSESSMENT TIP: TOTAL **10** POINTS

Name _____

A Special Day

Do any of these ideas spark memories of your own?

A fun trip

An accident

Playing on
a team

Moving to a
new place

Ideas for My Story About Myself

Write three to five ideas for a story about yourself.

_____

_____

_____

_____

_____

Think about each idea on your list.
Ask yourself these questions.

Can I remember this
experience clearly?

Why do I want to
write about it?

Circle the story idea you
want to write about.

Name

Do You Remember?

Close your eyes and picture your story.
Write notes that answer these questions.

Who else is in
your story?

Where does
it take place?

What happens?

Draw the most
important part of
your story in this circle.
Make your picture as
detailed as possible.

Name

Making It Better

• Revising Checklist •

Ask yourself these questions about your story.

❏ Does my story have a beginning, a middle, and an end?

❏ Does the beginning lead quickly into the main event?

❏ Do all my sentences keep to the topic?

❏ Did I use details so that my readers can picture what happened?

Questions for a Writing Conference

Use these questions to help you discuss your story with a classmate.

• What is best about this story?

• Does the story begin in an interesting way?

• Which parts do not keep to the topic?

• Which parts are hard to picture? What details are needed?

• How did the people feel? Are more details needed?

Write notes to help you remember the ideas from your writing conference.

My Notes

Name

A Great Place to Live

Write a magazine ad about the community you liked most in Community Ties. Fill out the chart to help you plan your ad.

List three things that you liked most about the people, places, and activities of the community you picked.

1 _____

2 _____

3 _____

Show what is special about the community.
Follow these directions:

1. Fold a sheet of drawing paper in half to make two magazine pages.

2. On one page, draw pictures of the three things you wrote about in the chart.

3. On the other page, write a slogan. Make your slogan a generalization. Include words such as *all*, *always*, *everyone*, *many*, or *most*.

4. On the same page as your slogan, write details about your pictures.

Checklist Use this list to check your work.
❏ My ad shows people, places, and activities.
❏ My slogan is a generalization.
❏ My ad gives details about the community.

ASSESSMENT TIP: SEE RUBRIC ON TEACHER'S BOOK P. 217A.

Name

Disaster!

Cut out a picture of a disaster from a
magazine or a newspaper and paste it on
this page. Then answer the questions.

1 What makes this event a disaster?

_____

_____

2 Why did the disaster occur?

_____

_____

3 Could anything have been done to prevent the disaster? If so, what?

_____

_____

Name

Disaster!

As you read each selection in Disaster!, fill in the boxes of the chart that apply to the selection.

Sample answers shown.

	What was unexpected about the disaster?	What did people learn from the disaster?
The *Titanic:* Lost … and Found	The *Titanic* hit an iceberg and sank. **(2 POINTS)**	1. Ships need enough lifeboats to carry everyone. 2. Ships need lifeboat drills. 3. Ships must keep their radios on to listen for calls for help. **(2)**
Pompeii … Buried Alive!	Mount Vesuvius erupted. **(2)**	1. Living by an active volcano can be dangerous. 2. Today we learn from the ruins what life was like in Pompeii. **(2)**
Patrick and the Great Molasses Explosion	A storage tank filled with molasses exploded. **(2)**	1. Storage tanks can be dangerous. 2. Disasters can happen anytime and anywhere. **(2)**

ASSESSMENT TIP: TOTAL **4** POINTS PER SELECTION

Name

Everybody Remain Calm

Read the ship's emergency instructions and answer the questions.
Sample answers shown.

To all passengers:

If there are any problems during this **voyage**, follow these instructions:

☆ Obey the captain's **orders** at all times.

☆ Head for the nearest lifeboat.

☆ When you are in a lifeboat, wait for the **rescue** ship to come to you.

☆ Don't panic. If you follow all of the instructions, we will all be

survivors.

1 Why would these instructions be for the **passengers**? The ship's crew
already knows what to do in case of any problems. **(2 POINTS)**

2 Why might someone go on a **voyage**? The person is moving to
someplace far away. **(2)**

3 Why should people follow the captain's **orders** at all times? The
captain knows what to do, and other people might not. **(2)**

4 How would a **rescue** ship do its job? A rescue ship would come to the
accident and pick up people from the sinking ship. **(2)**

5 Why would the people who don't panic be **survivors**? People who don't
panic follow instructions better, and they are more likely to do what is safe. **(2)**

ASSESSMENT TIP: TOTAL **10** POINTS

Name

Titanic Found!

Rewrite the article so that the details are correct.

Ballard Finds *Titanic*

Wire Report

Robert Ballard found the *Titanic* today. The *Titanic* had been lying on the bottom of the Pacific Ocean since April 15, 1972. On that day, while on its second voyage, the *Titanic* hit another ship and sank.

Luckily, the *Titanic* had enough lifeboats for all its passengers, so everybody on the ship survived. The survivors were brought to safety by helicopter.

Ballard's discovery is very exciting. Now Ballard says that he wants to bring the *Titanic* to the surface so that he can recover the *Titanic*'s treasure.

Sample: Robert Ballard found the *Titanic* today. The *Titanic* had been lying

on the bottom of the Atlantic Ocean since April 15, 1912. On that day, while on

its first voyage, the *Titanic* hit an iceberg and sank.

The *Titanic* did not have enough lifeboats for all its passengers, and only 705

survived. The survivors were rescued by a rescue ship.

Ballard's discovery is very exciting. He wants the *Titanic* to stay at the

bottom of the ocean because he wants her to be left in peace. **(10 POINTS)**

_____

_____

_____

_____

ASSESSMENT TIP: TOTAL **10** POINTS

Name

Treasure Hunt

Read the page from the instruction book. Write the topic of the page, the main idea of paragraph one, and three details that support the main idea.

How to Find Sunken Treasure

Patience is a very important part of hunting for sunken treasure. Often, you can search for many years and not find the treasure you want. You can sometimes find a small part of your treasure but still be far away from the main part. Sometimes, you can even see things that look like your treasure but really aren't.

When you have finally found your treasure, be very careful. Do not touch the treasure until you have taken pictures of it in the water. Keep a careful record of each piece of the treasure. The ship itself must be treated carefully because it can crumble if it is exposed to the air.

Topic

How to Find Sunken Treasure
(1 POINT)

Main Idea of Paragraph One

Patience is important. **(1)**

Supporting Details

You can search for many years and not find the treasure you want. You can find a small part of your treasure but not the main part. You may see things that look like your treasure but aren't. **(3)**

On a separate sheet of paper, copy and complete the graphic organizer for paragraph two. **(5)**

Name

Iceberg Ahead!

Find the sentences in the icebergs that have the same subjects. Write them as one sentence with a compound predicate.

Glaciers break apart.

The Coast Guard keeps an eye on icebergs.

An iceberg's ice is very hard.

Icebergs come from glaciers.

Glaciers push toward the sea.

The Coast Guard warns ships about them.

An iceberg's ice can be over a thousand years old.

Icebergs are made of fresh water.

Sample sentences shown. Some predicates could be reversed.

1 ___Icebergs come from glaciers and are made of fresh water. **(2.5 POINTS)**
_____

2 ___Glaciers push toward the sea and break apart. **(2.5)**
_____

3 ___An iceberg's ice is very hard and can be over a thousand years old. **(2.5)**
_____

4 ___The Coast Guard keeps an eye on icebergs and warns ships about them.

___**(2.5)**
_____

ASSESSMENT TIP: TOTAL **10** POINTS

Silver Lining

The sinking of the *Titanic* was a disaster, but it had one good
result. Find out what that result was by solving the puzzle.
For each definition, write a word made from a base word
in the box and the ending *-er* or *-est*. Then write each
numbered letter on the line with the matching number.

teach	strong	hard	fast	heavy
smart	hike	sleepy	pitch	travel

1 weighing more   h e a v i e r **(1 POINT)**
                               2

2 one who goes on a trip   t r a v e l e r   **(1)**
                                                    5

3 moving most quickly   f a s t e s t   **(1)**
                             3

4 more tired   s l e e p i e r   **(1)**
                                9

5 one who climbs a mountain   h i k e r   **(1)**
                                   7

6 one who helps others learn   t e a c h e r   **(1)**
                                        4

7 more wise   s m a r t e r   **(1)**
                   6

8 one who throws to a batter   p i t c h e r   **(1)**
                                       8

9 most difficult   h a r d e s t   **(1)**
                                      10

10 most powerful   s t r o n g e s t   **(1)**
                        1

What the world gained from the *Titanic* disaster:

s a f e r   s h i p s
1 2 3 4 5   6 7 8 9 10

Name _____

Loading the Ship

Fill in the levels of the ship with the correct words. Some words can fit in more than one level. Then add some of your own words to each level.

Sample answers shown.

captain	crow's-nest
decks	lifeboats
passengers	rescue ship
submarine	survivors
voyage	

Things That Go in Water

1. rescue ship **(1 POINT)**
2. submarine **(1)**
3. lifeboats **(1)**
4. rowboat **(1)**
5. raft **(1)**

Words That Mean "Trip"

1. voyage **(1)**
2. journey **(1)**

Parts of a Ship

1. crow's-nest **(1)**
2. decks **(1)**
3. sails **(1)**
4. cabins **(1)**

People on a Ship

1. captain **(1)**
2. passengers **(1)**
3. survivors **(1)**
4. sailors **(1)**

People Who Give Orders

1. captain **(1)**
2. first mate **(1)**
3. boss **(1)**

ASSESSMENT TIP: TOTAL **18** POINTS

Name

Safe and Sound

The Vowel Sound in *saw* Each Spelling Word has the vowel sound that you hear in *saw.* This sound is written as lôl. It can be spelled with the pattern **aw, a before l, ough,** or **augh.**

lôl   s**aw**   t**a**lk   th**ough**t   c**augh**t

Help save the passengers! Write the Spelling Words that match the pattern for the lôl sound shown on each lifeboat.

Spelling Words

1. saw
2. talk
3. small
4. thought
5. law
6. caught
7. fought
8. taught

My Study List What other words do you need to study for spelling? Add them to My Study List for *The Titanic: Lost . . . and Found* in the back of this book.

aw

1 saw **(1 POINT)**

2 law **(1)**

ough

5 thought **(1)**

6 fought **(1)**

a before l

3 talk **(1)**

4 small **(1)**

augh

7 caught **(1)**

8 taught **(1)**

ASSESSMENT TIP: TOTAL **8** POINTS

Disaster!   95

....
Name

Spelling Spree

Proofreading Find and circle four
misspelled Spelling Words in these
headlines. Then write each word correctly.
Begin each word with a capital letter.

**Ship's Radio (Cawt) Sinking Boat's Signal
for Help**

1 Caught **(1 POINT)**
_____

**Rescuers Saw (Smal) Boats in Time to Save
Hundreds of People!**

2 Small **(1)**
_____

Sailors (Faught) to Have More Lifeboat Drills

3 Fought **(1)**
_____

New (Lawe) Passed to Make Ships Safer

4 Law **(1)**
_____

Safety Senses Write a Spelling Word to complete each
sentence in this part of a news story.

    After the ship sank, a teenage girl __(5)__ a little boy fall out of a
lifeboat. The girl had been __(6)__ what to do in swim class, so she
held an oar out to the __(7)__ boy. He __(8)__ hold of it and was pulled
to safety. The teenager would not __(9)__ to reporters. However, the
boy said that he __(10)__ the girl should get a medal.

5 saw **(1)**   **7** small **(1)**   **9** talk **(1)**
_____   _____   _____

6 taught **(1)** **8** caught **(1)** **10** thought **(1)**
_____   _____   _____

SOS Your ship sank and you're on an island. On a separate
sheet of paper, tell what happened and where you are. Use
Spelling Words from the list.

ASSESSMENT TIP: TOTAL **10** POINTS

Name

Voyage of the Verbs

Singular Noun in the Subject
A flag waves.

Plural Noun in the Subject
Many flags wave.

Verbs in the Present Read each sentence. Write the
correct present-time form of the verb in ( ).

1 The *Titanic* __sits **(1 POINT)**__ on the ocean bottom. (sit)

2 Scientists __try **(1)**__ a different route. (try)

3 Robert Ballard __invents **(1)**__ a special underwater robot. (invent)

4 The *Argo* __dives **(1)**__ very, very deep. (dive)

5 The *Argo* __reaches **(1)**__ the sea bottom. (reach)

6 The robot __pushes **(1)**__ away the sand. (push)

7 A fish __passes **(1)**__ by the ship. (pass)

8 The explorers __find **(1)**__ the *Titanic*! (find)

9 Giant anchors __rest **(1)**__ in the sand. (rest)

10 The message __asks **(1)**__ that the ship be left in peace. (ask)

Name _____

Disasters in the Present

Verbs in the Present Picture in your mind a disaster at sea. First, draw your scene on the canvas.

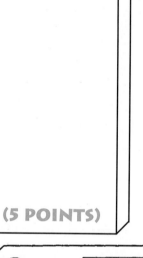

(5 POINTS)

Next, write at least five complete sentences about your picture. Use a verb in present time in each sentence. Use three verbs from the suggestion box.   Answers will vary.

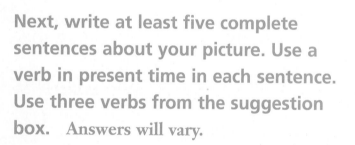

Suggestion Box

The captain	One lookout
carries	Two sailors
hurry	float
A radio operator	Icebergs
rescues	swim

_____

_____

_____

_____

_____

(5)

ASSESSMENT TIP: TOTAL **10** POINTS

Name

Outburst!

Words are erupting from this volcano! Cut out and paste
the words next to their meanings.

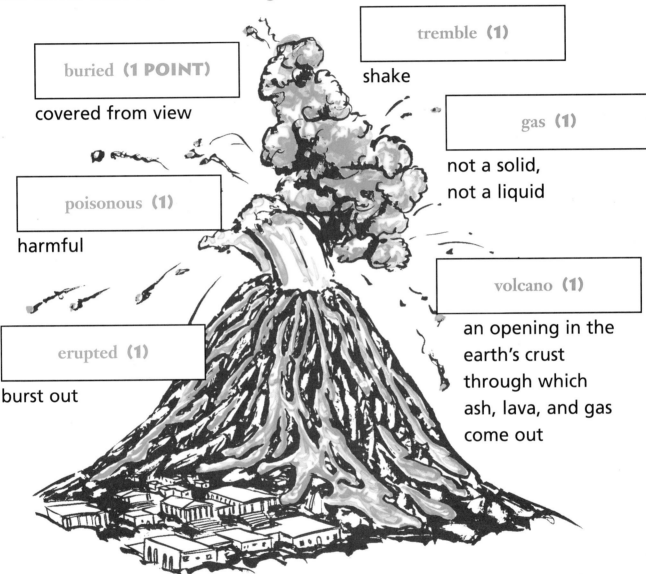

buried **(1 POINT)**

covered from view

tremble **(1)**

shake

poisonous **(1)**

harmful

gas **(1)**

not a solid,
not a liquid

erupted **(1)**

burst out

volcano **(1)**

an opening in the
earth's crust
through which
ash, lava, and gas
come out

Use these words to write about a volcano on the back of this sheet. **(4)**

volcano	gas	erupted
tremble	poisonous	buried

Write about a volcano.

_____

_____

_____

_____

_____

_____

_____

_____

_____

_____

_____

_____

_____

Name

Trapped in Time

Finish the index cards.   Sample answers shown.

Three things people in Pompeii did every day were

go to the baths, visit the market,

and pray in the temples.

(3 POINTS)

_____

_____

Three things that happened when Vesuvius erupted were

gas and melted rock came

pouring out, people ran for

cover, and people ran to the

temples to pray. **(3)**

_____

_____

We know about Pompeii because

Pliny saw it and wrote a

description of it; scientists have

discovered many things from the

ruins. **(2)**

_____

Two things that scientists found were

gold bracelets and unbroken

eggs. **(2)**

_____

_____

ASSESSMENT TIP: TOTAL **10** POINTS

Name

Post Card from Pompeii

Read the post card. Find four facts and four opinions. Write them in the chart. Then answer the question.

Dear Jeff,

Pompeii is a very interesting place to visit. It was once covered with volcanic ash. But scientists have done a good job of uncovering it. They have found jewelry and unbroken eggs here. They even found a mosaic that says "Beware of Dog" in Latin. These aren't even the most amazing parts of Pompeii. The city has been partially rebuilt. You should try to visit Pompeii.

See you soon!

María

FACTS	OPINIONS
It was once covered with volcanic ash. **(1 POINT)**	Pompeii is a very interesting place to visit. **(1)**
They have found jewelry and unbroken eggs here. **(1)**	Scientists have done a good job of uncovering it. **(1)**
They even found a mosaic that says "Beware of Dog" in Latin. **(1)**	These aren't even the most amazing parts of Pompeii. **(1)**
The city has been partially rebuilt. **(1)**	You should try to visit Pompeii. **(1)**

What are two ways you can prove these facts?

Sample: Go to Pompeii; look in an encyclopedia **(2)**

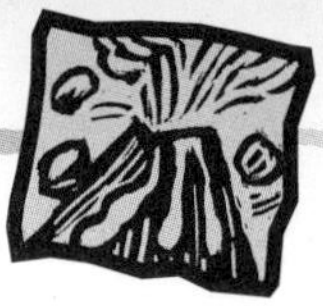

Name

Can You Explain It?

Use this page to plan your explanation. Then number the facts in the order you will use them.

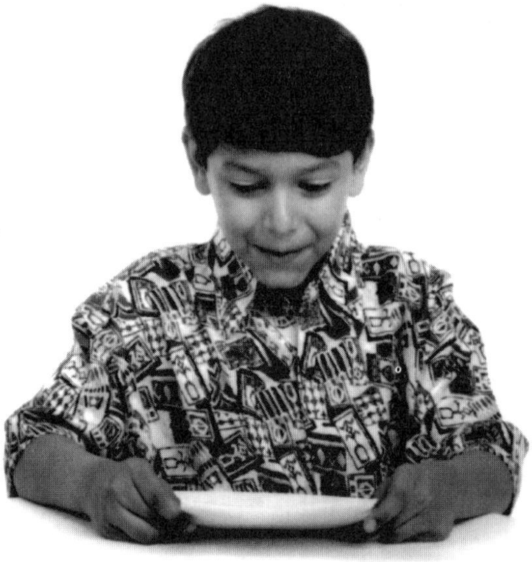

Topic:

Topic Sentence:

Fact:

Fact:

Fact:

Fact:

Name

Dig It!

To find out what the scientists uncovered at Pompeii, solve the puzzle. First, divide each word into two syllables. Write the syllables on the lines with the dot between them.

1 captures ___cap___ • ___tures___ **(2 POINTS)**
                                            5

2 mainland ___main___ • ___land___ **(2)**
                        6

3 subjects ___sub___ • ___jects___ **(2)**
                                        3

4 mammals ___mam___ • ___mals___ **(2)**
                                        9

5 picnic ___pic___ • ___nic___ **(2)**
                    4

6 purple ___pur___ • ___ple___ **(2)**
                                    7

7 annoy ___an___ • ___noy___ **(2)**
                1

8 explode ___ex___ • ___plode___ **(2)**

9 oblong ___ob___ • ___long___ **(2)**
                    2

10 anger ___an___ • ___ger___ **(2)**
                8

Write each numbered syllable on the line with the matching number.

What the scientists found:

___an___ •cient ___ob___ • ___jects___ ,
    1   2   3

___pic___ • ___tures___ , and the re• ___main___ s
   4   5   6

of peo• ___ple___ and ___an___ •i• ___mals___
            7   8   9

ASSESSMENT TIP: TOTAL **20** POINTS

Name

Pompeii Puzzle

Complete the puzzle by using the clues.

| ashes | buried | enormous | erupted | pebbles | poisonous |
| sealed | skeletons | spilled | trapped | tremble | volcano |

Across

2. Groups of bones

5. What Vesuvius did

7. Some people of Pompeii were ____ under rocks and ashes from Vesuvius.

9. Shake violently

10. Dusty material that came out of Vesuvius

11. A cloud of ____ gas came out of Vesuvius.

Down

1. Shut tightly

2. Poured out

3. Caught

4. Little, tiny rocks

6. Very large

8. An explosive mountain

ASSESSMENT TIP: TOTAL **12** POINTS
(**1** POINT FOR EACH ANSWER)

Disaster!

Name

Dark Days

Vowel + r Sounds Each Spelling Word has a vowel sound + *r*. The vowel + *r* sounds you hear in *dark* are written as |är|. They can be spelled with the pattern *ar*.

|är| d**ar**k

The vowel + *r* sounds you hear in *near* are written as |îr|. They can be spelled with the pattern *ear*.

|îr| n**ear**

The vowel + *r* sounds you hear in *more* are written as |ôr|. They can be spelled with the patterns *or* and *ore*.

|ôr| st**ory**   m**ore**

Write each Spelling Word on the cloud with the matching vowel sound.

|är|

1. dark **(1 POINT)**
   _____
2. start **(1)**
   _____
3. part **(1)**
   _____

|îr|

4. near **(1)**
   _____
5. year **(1)**
   _____

|ôr|

6. more **(1)**
   _____
7. story **(1)**
   _____
8. morning **(1)**
   _____

ASSESSMENT TIP: TOTAL **8** POINTS

Spelling Spree

Only Opposites The second part of each clue is the opposite of the first part. Write the Spelling Word that fits each clue.

1 not far, but _____near_____ **(1 POINT)**

2 not light, but _____dark_____ **(1)**

3 not whole, but _____part_____ **(1)**

4 not stop, but _____start_____ **(1)**

5 not evening, but _____morning_____ **(1)**

6 not less, but _____more_____ **(1)**

Proofreading Find and circle four misspelled Spelling Words on this sign at a museum. Then write each word correctly.

> One (morening) near the town of Pompeii, Mount Vesuvius blew its top. Ashes piled up higher than the second (storey) of some houses. Thick, (darck) clouds filled the sky. In two days the whole town was buried. More than a (yeer) later the volcano still erupted, but Pompeii was gone.

7 ___morning___ **(1)**

8 ___story___ **(1)**

9 ___dark___ **(1)**

10 ___year___ **(1)**

Danger Signs On a separate sheet of paper, draw three signs to warn people of danger. Below each sign, write one or two sentences that tell what the sign means. Use Spelling Words from the list.

ASSESSMENT TIP: TOTAL **10** POINTS

Name _____

Explosion!

Present	Spelling Change	Past Time
melt	+ ed	melt**ed**
explode	– e + ed	explod**ed**
drop	+ p + ed	drop**ped**
hurry	– y + i + ed	hurr**ied**

Read the sentences. Write the correct past time form of the verb in ( ) to complete each sentence.

1 The falling rock _____*crushed* **(1 PT.)**_____ everything in its path. (crush)

2 The family _____*carried* **(1)**_____ their best silver and dishes. (carry)

3 Some people _____*saved* **(1)**_____ nothing from the burning ashes. (save)

4 Others _____*cried* **(1)**_____ for help from the gods. (cry)

5 The shower of hot ashes _____*lasted* **(1)**_____ a long time. (last)

6 The rumbling finally _____*stopped* **(1)**_____. (stop)

7 Someone _____*tried* **(1)**_____ to save a lost dog. (try)

8 We _____*learned* **(1)**_____ a terrible lesson about the volcanoes. (learn)

9 Across the bay, a boy _____*gazed* **(1)**_____ at the strange sight. (gaze)

10 His letters _____*described* **(1)**_____ the disaster of Pompeii. (describe)

ASSESSMENT TIP: TOTAL **10** POINTS

Name

Uncovering the Past

Help scientists uncover the ruins of Pompeii. Choose the right tool for forming the past time verb. Every time you write a correct verb, you get closer to Pompeii. The first stone has been uncovered for you.

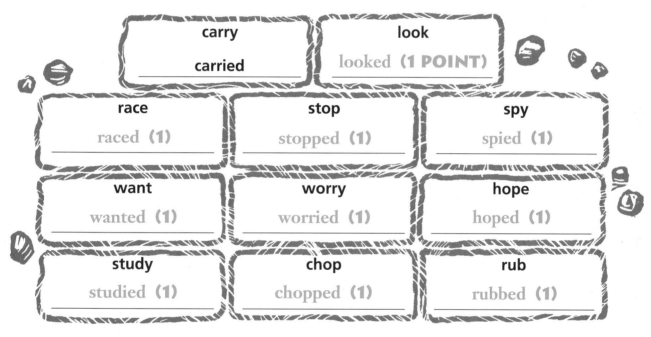

carry	look
carried	looked **(1 POINT)**

race	stop	spy
raced **(1)**	stopped **(1)**	spied **(1)**

want	worry	hope
wanted **(1)**	worried **(1)**	hoped **(1)**

study	chop	rub
studied **(1)**	chopped **(1)**	rubbed **(1)**

Write sentences for five of the verbs you wrote.   Answers will vary.

1 _____

2 _____

3 _____

4 _____

5 _____ **(10)**

ASSESSMENT TIP: TOTAL **20** POINTS

Disaster! **109**

This Is What I Can Do!

Topic Ideas

How to . . .
feed my cat
check out a book from the library
use the computer's Cut and Paste features
make a paper airplane
grow crystals
make a piñata
weave a belt
make a rubber stamp
play dodge ball

My Ideas
Write three to five things you know how to do well.

1 _____

2 _____

3 _____

4 _____

5 _____

Think about each idea.
Ask yourself these
questions.

Circle the idea you
want to write about.

> Can I explain all of
> the steps clearly?

> Do I really want
> to write about
> this topic?

> Do I know
> exactly how
> to do this?

Step by Step

Write your topic. Then make notes in words or pictures to answer each question.

My topic is _____

What materials are needed? _____

_____

What are the steps?

Step 1

Step 2

Step 3

Step 4

Step 5

Name

Take Another Look

Reread and revise your instructions.

Revising Checklist

Use these questions to help you revise your paper.

❑ Did I begin my instructions with a topic sentence?

❑ Did I include all steps?

❑ Did I give complete details?

❑ Is the order of the steps correct?

❑ Did I use order words?

Questions for a Writing Conference

Use these questions to discuss your paper with a classmate.

• What do you like about these instructions?

• Is it clear what the instructions are for?

• Are sizes, amounts, and colors of the materials given?

• Are the steps complete and in order?

• What other information is needed?

Notes from My Writing Conference with

_____
Classmate's Name

_____

_____

_____

_____

_____

_____

Name

Sticky Scene

Use the words to describe what you see in the picture. Sample answers shown.

| gooey | molasses | barrels | craving | pitcher |

Two barrels of molasses tipped over in a store. A dog is licking up the

molasses. The owner of the store is stuck in the gooey molasses. A boy who

has a craving for molasses is scooping some up with a pitcher.

ASSESSMENT TIP: TOTAL **10** POINTS
(**2** POINTS FOR EACH CORRECTLY USED WORD)

Name

Map Madness

Write which characters were at each place and what they were doing when the molasses tank exploded.

The Loading Docks

Patrick's father was there. He was sitting on a dock eating his lunch. **(5 POINTS)**

Outside the Molasses Store

Patrick was there. He was getting molasses to take home to his mother. **(5)**

Patrick's House

Patrick's mother and sister were there. His mother was taking care of his sister, who bumped her head when the tank exploded. **(5)**

ASSESSMENT TIP: TOTAL **15** POINTS

Name _____

A Sweet Story

Cut and paste the correct picture in the box. Then complete each statement of cause and effect.

Cause: Mom wants to make molasses oatmeal cookies but has no more molasses.

Effect: ___You go with your mother to___ get molasses. **(5 POINTS)**

Effect: The cookie dough becomes sweet and tasty.

Cause: ___You add molasses to the___ cookie dough. **(5)**

Effect: ___The cookies come out___ burned. **(5)**

Cause: ___You eat too many cookies.___ **(5)**

Cause: Mom leaves the cookies in the oven too long.

Effect: You get a stomachache.

Name

What Is Molasses?

Read this description of molasses. Then answer the questions in complete sentences.

Molasses is a thick brown syrup made from sugar cane. It is used in making candy and baked goods. Farmers also use molasses as food for livestock.

Sugar cane is a tall grass that grows in warm places such as Florida, Cuba, and Hawaii. The plants can be as much as fifteen feet high. Their long stalks contain a sweet juice.

To make sugar, the juice of the sugar cane is boiled several times. After being heated and reheated, the juice forms sugar crystals, but there is still some juice left over. That juice is called *molasses*.

1 What are the uses of molasses? Molasses is used in making candy and baked goods. Farmers use it to feed livestock. **(5 POINTS)**

2 What plant is molasses made from? Molasses is made from sugar cane. **(5)**

3 Where does this plant grow? The sugar cane plant grows in warm places such as Florida, Cuba, and Hawaii. **(5)**

4 How is the juice of this plant turned into molasses? Molasses is made from sugar cane juice which has been boiled several times. After it has been heated and reheated, the juice forms crystals. The juice left over is molasses. **(5)**

ASSESSMENT TIP: TOTAL **20** POINTS

Disaster! 117

Name

A Sticky Situation

Each numbered word has a synonym hidden in the puzzle. The words can be read from top to bottom, from left to right, or diagonally. Circle each synonym, and write it in the blanks.

1 sugary   s w e e t   **(1 POINT)**

2 surprised   a m a z e d   **(1)**

3 mad   a n g r y   **(1)**

4 thin   n a r r o w   **(1)**

5 impolite   r u d e   **(1)**

6 small   l i t t l e   **(1)**

7 beneath   b e l o w   **(1)**

8 cut   s l i c e   **(1)**

```
W  A  M  E  T  B  K  G  V
A  N  G  R  Y  O  F  S  B
L  A  N  C  D  S  W  L  E
D  R  M  P  U  L  B  I  L
I  R  Q  A  V  I  S  T  O
C  O  F  D  Z  C  J  T  W
S  W  E  E  T  E  M  L  S
B  J  I  G  R  U  D  E  U
```

ASSESSMENT TIP:
TOTAL **8** POINTS

Name _____

Dinner Is Served!

Complete the menu by filling in the blanks.

barrels	brag	sweetened	craving
fondness	gooey	slurped	
molasses	pitcher	rumbling	

MENU

MAIN COURSES

Monster Turkey Sandwich $4.25

No matter how hungry you are, this dish

will satisfy your _craving_ **(1 POINT)**.

Jumbo Chef's Salad $4.75

If you have a _fondness_ **(1)** _____

for salad and your stomach is

rumbling **(1)** _____, this is

for you!

SIDE DISHES

French Fries $1.00

We don't like to _brag_ **(1)** _____,

but these are the best.

Pickles $1.50

The best pickles are those from our

own private _barrels_ **(1)** _____.

MENU

DESSERT

Better-Than-Sugar Cake $4.75

This is even better than cake

sweetened **(1)** _____ with sugar. It's made

from pure _molasses_ **(1)** _____.

Ice Cream Sundae $2.25

If you have ever had our

gooey **(1)** _____ fudge sauce, we're

sure you _slurped_ **(1)** _____ it up!

DRINKS

Soda   glass $ .75

pitcher **(1)** _____ $2.50

Name some foods you'd like to see

added to this menu. _____

_____

_____

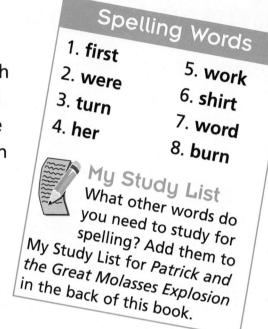

Name

Sticky Stuff

The Vowel + *r* Sounds in *first* Each Spelling Word has the vowel + *r* sounds that you hear in *first*. These sounds are written as |ûr|. They can be spelled with the pattern *er, ir, ur,* or *or*.

|ûr| w**er**e   f**ir**st   t**ur**n   w**or**k

Help people find what they lost in the molasses! Write each Spelling Word on the item that has the matching spelling for the |ûr| sounds.

Spelling Words

1. **first**
2. **were**
3. **turn**
4. **her**
5. **work**
6. **shirt**
7. **word**
8. **burn**

My Study List
What other words do you need to study for spelling? Add them to My Study List for *Patrick and the Great Molasses Explosion* in the back of this book.

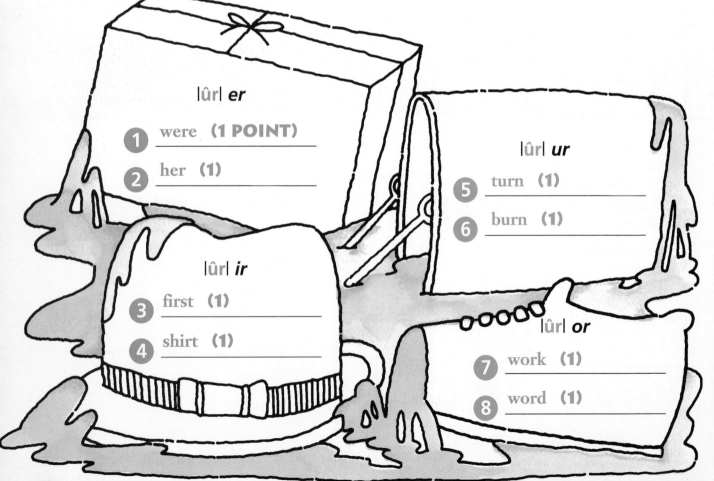

|ûr| **er**

1 were   **(1 POINT)**

2 her   **(1)**

|ûr| **ir**

3 first   **(1)**

4 shirt   **(1)**

|ûr| **ur**

5 turn   **(1)**

6 burn   **(1)**

|ûr| **or**

7 work   **(1)**

8 word   **(1)**

ASSESSMENT TIP: TOTAL **8** POINTS

Name _____

Spelling Spree

Proofreading Find and circle four misspelled Spelling Words in this girl's story about the explosion. Then write each word correctly.

Spelling Words

1. first
2. were
3. turn
4. her
5. work
6. shirt
7. word
8. burn

Mother and I wer hanging up the wash in the backyard. First came a boom and then a wave of molasses. Down went the clothesline! Mother's shert was covered with sticky molasses. So was hir hair. Mother was so surprised that she couldn't say a wurd!

1 ___were___ **(1 POINT)**

2 ___shirt___ **(1)**

3 ___her___ **(1)**

4 ___word___ **(1)**

I Was There! Write a Spelling Word to complete each statement about the molasses explosion.

I saw a building catch fire and __(5)__.

I was the __(7)__ person to call the police.

I was on my way to __(6)__ when the explosion happened.

I couldn't __(8)__ my horse in time. He got stuck!

5 ___burn___ **(1)**

6 ___work___ **(1)**

7 ___first___ **(1)**

8 ___turn___ **(1)**

Many Thanks Patrick never got to thank the man who saved him. Imagine that someone has just saved you. On a separate sheet of paper, write a short letter to thank that person. Use Spelling Words from the list.

ASSESSMENT TIP: TOTAL **8** POINTS

Disaster!  121

Name

"Be" Tankful

The Verb *be* Help
Patrick get the molasses out of the tank. Cross off each verb on the tank when you use it to complete a sentence. When you have used all the words, the tank will be empty.

Subject	Present	Past
I	am	was
you	are	were
he, she, it, singular noun	is	was
we, they	are	were
plural noun	are	were

1. The tank __is (1 POINT)__ full of sticky molasses. (am, is)

2. I __am (1)__ afraid of an accident. (am, are)

3. You __were (1)__ also hungry for molasses cookies. (was, were)

4. The workers on the dock __are (1)__ heroes. (am, are)

5. We __were (1)__ in shock over the molasses flood. (was, were)

6. I __was (1)__ late for school again. (was, were)

7. It __was (1)__ everywhere. (was, were)

8. The horses __were (1)__ upset by this accident. (was, were)

9. You __are (1)__ a brave young man. (are, is)

10. They __are (1)__ sick of molasses. (are, is)

ASSESSMENT TIP: TOTAL **10** POINTS

Name

Beautiful Molassesland

Study the map of a country called Molassesland. Complete the answers to the questions. Use the correct form of *be*.

| am |
| is |
| are |
| was |
| were |

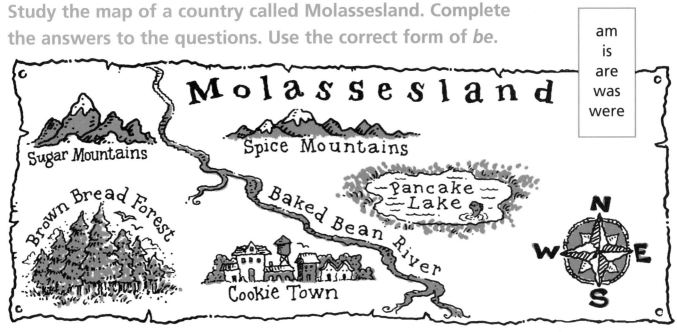

1 What country is this?

This country ___is Molassesland   **(2 POINTS)**___.

2 What mountains are west of Molassesland?

Those mountains ___are the Sugar Mountains   **(2)**___.

3 What is the name of the lake?

The lake ___is Pancake Lake   **(2)**___.

4 Is Cookie Town north or south of the river?

Cookie Town ___is south of the river   **(2)**___.

5 Are you sure you have never been to Molassesland?

I ___am sure   **(2)**___.

On a separate sheet of paper, write five sentences about a trip to Molassesland. Use *was* and *were*.

ASSESSMENT TIP: TOTAL **10** POINTS   **Disaster!** **123**

Name

A Letter to the Captain

Write to the captain of the *Titanic*. Tell him what he should have done to prevent the disaster. Fill out the chart to help plan your letter.

What actions helped cause the disaster? List at least three.

1 _____

2 _____

3 _____

4 _____

List your opinions of what should have been done to avoid the problems.

1 _____

2 _____

3 _____

4 _____

Use the information you listed to write your letter to the captain. Present your work to your class or group. Use the checklist to make sure that you are ready to share your letter.

Checklist

☐ My letter shows that I understand the *Titanic* disaster.
☐ My letter gives facts about three actions that helped cause the disaster.
☐ My letter gives my opinions about what should have been done to prevent the disaster.

ASSESSMENT TIP: SEE RUBRIC ON
TEACHER'S BOOK P. 309A.

STUDENT
HANDBOOK

Contents

MY READING LOG

Use this log to record the books or other materials you read on your own.

Date ______________________________

Author ______________________________

Title ______________________________

Notes and Comments ______________________________

____

____

____

____

Date ______________________________

Author ______________________________

Title ______________________________

Notes and Comments ______________________________

____

____

____

____

Date _____

Author _____

Title _____

Notes and Comments _____

_____

_____

_____

Date _____

Author _____

Title _____

Notes and Comments _____

_____

_____

_____

Date _____

Author _____

Title _____

Notes and Comments _____

_____

_____

_____

Date _____

Author _____

Title _____

Notes and Comments _____

_____

_____

_____

_____

Date _____

Author _____

Title _____

Notes and Comments _____

_____

_____

_____

_____

Date _____

Author _____

Title _____

Notes and Comments _____

_____

_____

_____

_____

Date _____

Author _____

Title _____

Notes and Comments _____

_____

_____

_____

_____

Date _____

Author _____

Title _____

Notes and Comments _____

_____

_____

_____

_____

Date _____

Author _____

Title _____

Notes and Comments _____

_____

_____

_____

_____

How to Study a Word

1 **LOOK** at the word.
- What does the word mean?
- What letters are in the word?
- Name and touch each letter.

2 **SAY** the word.
- Listen for the consonant sounds.
- Listen for the vowel sounds.

3 **THINK** about the word.
- How is each sound spelled?
- Close your eyes and picture the word.
- What familiar spelling patterns do you see?
- What other words have the same spelling patterns?

4 **WRITE** the word.
- Think about the sounds and the letters.
- Form the letters correctly.

5 **CHECK** the spelling.
- Did you spell the word the same way it is spelled in your word list?
- If you did not spell the word correctly, write the word again.

WORDS OFTEN MISSPELLED

above	cough	half	o'clock	thought
again	could	have	of	through
already	country	head	often	to
answer	daily	heard	ought	toe
any	daughter	heart	pear	too
are	dead	heavy	people	touch
bear	death	helpful	picnic	traveling
beautiful	do	I	pink	trouble
been	does	island	pretty	two
believe	doesn't	judge	rebuild	until
beyond	dollar	July	roar	unusual
blue	done	June	rolling	voice
both	door	key	rough	want
bought	double	large	rule	warm
boxing	dying	laugh	said	was
bread	early	let's	school	wash
break	electric	libraries	sew	watch
breakfast	enough	listen	some	weigh
breath	eye	live	son	what
brother	falling	lose	spread	where
brought	feet	love	straight	who
buy	fought	lying	sure	woman
caught	friend	many	taught	won
ceiling	from	message	tear	wonderful
certain	front	money	teeth	won't
chief	ghost	move	their	word
children	give	neighbor	there	work
choice	glove	noise	they	worried
color	gone	no one	they're	you
comb	great	none	think	young
come	guess	nothing	though	your

The Three Little Hawaiian Pigs and the Magic Shark

Spelling Long *a* and Long *e*

|ā| → t**ai**l, pl**ay**

|ē| → b**ea**ch, thr**ee**

Spelling Words

1. three
2. tail
3. beach
4. play
5. deep
6. away
7. please
8. chain

Challenge Words

1. easy
2. really
3. reef
4. creature

My Study List

Add your own spelling words on the back.

133

The Three Little Javelinas

Vowel-Consonant-*e*

|ā| → sh**ade**

|ē| → th**ese**

|ī| → m**ice**

|ō| → n**ose**

|oo͞| or |yoo͞| → **use**

Spelling Words

1. nose
2. these
3. shade
4. use
5. mice
6. smoke
7. snake
8. ripe

Challenge Words

1. escape
2. amaze
3. arrive
4. fortune

My Study List

Add your own spelling words on the back.

133

The Three Little Wolves and the Big, Bad Pig

Short Vowels

|ă| → **a**sk

|ĕ| → n**e**xt

|ĭ| → m**i**x

|ŏ| → l**o**ck

|ŭ| → sh**u**t

Spelling Words

1. ask
2. next
3. mix
4. smell
5. black
6. shut
7. lock
8. truck

Challenge Words

1. knock
2. scent
3. plenty
4. fetch

My Study List

Add your own spelling words on the back.

133

Name _____

 My Study List

1. _____
2. _____
3. _____
4. _____
5. _____
6. _____
7. _____
8. _____
9. _____
10. _____

Selection Vocabulary

You may want to use these
words in your own writing.

1. prowling
2. grunted
3. crumbled
4. trembling
5. scorched

How to Study a Word

LOOK at the word.
SAY the word.
THINK about the word.
WRITE the word.
CHECK the spelling.

134

Name _____

 My Study List

1. _____
2. _____
3. _____
4. _____
5. _____
6. _____
7. _____
8. _____
9. _____
10. _____

Selection Vocabulary

You may want to use these
words in your own writing.

1. desert
2. dust storm
3. whirlwind
4. tumbleweeds
5. cactus
6. adobe

How to Study a Word

LOOK at the word.
SAY the word.
THINK about the word.
WRITE the word.
CHECK the spelling.

134

Name _____

 My Study List

1. _____
2. _____
3. _____
4. _____
5. _____
6. _____
7. _____
8. _____
9. _____
10. _____

Selection Vocabulary

You may want to use these
words in your own writing.

1. craving
2. anxiously
3. plot
4. scheme
5. pangs
6. furious

How to Study a Word

LOOK at the word.
SAY the word.
THINK about the word.
WRITE the word.
CHECK the spelling.

134

When Jo Louis Won the Title

The Vowel Sounds in *town* and *boy*

|oul| ➤ t**ow**n, pr**ou**d
|oil| ➤ n**oi**se, b**oy**

Spelling Words

1. town
2. boy
3. proud
4. crowd
5. noise
6. round
7. voice
8. toy

Challenge Words

1. mountain
2. enjoy
3. annoy
4. thousand

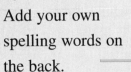

My Study List

Add your own spelling words on the back. ➤

Family Pictures

The Vowel Sounds in *cook* and *knew*

|ŏŏ| ➤ c**oo**k, p**u**t
|o͞o| ➤ kn**ew**, b**oo**th

Spelling Words

1. cook
2. knew
3. put
4. woods
5. pull
6. booth
7. coop
8. drew

Challenge Words

1. neighborhood
2. afternoon
3. balloon
4. crooked

My Study List

Add your own spelling words on the back. ➤

A Fruit and Vegetable Man

Spelling Long *i* and Long *o*

|ī| ➤ r**igh**t, t**ie**
|ō| ➤ s**oa**p, **ow**n

Spelling Words

1. own
2. right
3. own
4. might
5. tie
6. soap
7. pie
8. float

Challenge Words

1. sigh
2. flown
3. delight
4. follow

My Study List

Add your own spelling words on the back. ➤

Name _____

My Study List

1. _____
2. _____
3. _____
4. _____
5. _____
6. _____
7. _____
8. _____
9. _____
10. _____

Selection Vocabulary

You may want to use these words in your own writing.

1. market
2. pyramids
3. diamonds
4. accent
5. designs
6. triangles

How to Study a Word

LOOK at the word.
SAY the word.
THINK about the word.
WRITE the word.
CHECK the spelling.

Name _____

My Study List

1. _____
2. _____
3. _____
4. _____
5. _____
6. _____
7. _____
8. _____
9. _____
10. _____

Selection Vocabulary

You may want to use these words in your own writing.

1. recognize
2. scene
3. custom
4. inspired

How to Study a Word

LOOK at the word.
SAY the word.
THINK about the word.
WRITE the word.
CHECK the spelling.

Name _____

My Study List

1. _____
2. _____
3. _____
4. _____
5. _____
6. _____
7. _____
8. _____
9. _____
10. _____

Selection Vocabulary

You may want to use these words in your own writing.

1. whirled
2. tattered
3. bellowed
4. title fight
5. title
6. braced

How to Study a Word

LOOK at the word.
SAY the word.
THINK about the word.
WRITE the word.
CHECK the spelling.

Patrick and the Great Molasses Explosion

Pompeii...Buried Alive!

The Titanic: Lost...And Found

The Vowel + r Sounds in *first*

lûl ➔ w**er**e, f**ir**st, t**ur**n
w**or**k

Vowels + r Sounds

läl	➔	d**ark**
lîl	➔	n**ear**
lôl	➔	st**or**y, m**or**e

The Vowel Sound in *saw*

lôl ➔ s**aw**, t**al**k, th**ough**t, c**augh**t

Spelling Words

1. first
2. were
3. turn
4. her
5. work
6. shirt
7. word
8. burn

Spelling Words

1. dark
2. more
3. start
4. story
5. near
6. morning
7. part
8. year

Spelling Words

1. saw
2. talk
3. small
4. thought
5. law
6. caught
7. fought
8. taught

Challenge Words

1. stern
2. hurry
3. perfect
4. thorough

Challenge Words

1. horrible
2. enormous
3. explore
4. argue

Challenge Words

1. already
2. flaw
3. although
4. daughter

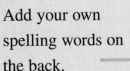

My Study List

Add your own spelling words on the back. ➔

My Study List

Add your own spelling words on the back. ➔

My Study List

Add your own spelling words on the back. ➔

Name_____

 My Study List

1. _____
2. _____
3. _____
4. _____
5. _____
6. _____
7. _____
8. _____
9. _____
10. _____

Selection Vocabulary

You may want to use these words in your own writing.

1. passengers
2. voyage
3. orders
4. rescue
5. survivors

How to Study a Word

LOOK at the word.
SAY the word.
THINK about the word.
WRITE the word.
CHECK the spelling.

Name_____

 My Study List

1. _____
2. _____
3. _____
4. _____
5. _____
6. _____
7. _____
8. _____
9. _____
10. _____

Selection Vocabulary

You may want to use these words in your own writing.

1. volcano
2. erupted
3. gas
4. poisonous
5. tremble
6. buried

How to Study a Word

LOOK at the word.
SAY the word.
THINK about the word.
WRITE the word.
CHECK the spelling.

Name_____

 My Study List

1. _____
2. _____
3. _____
4. _____
5. _____
6. _____
7. _____
8. _____
9. _____
10. _____

Selection Vocabulary

You may want to use these words in your own writing.

1. molasses
2. gooey
3. barrels
4. pitcher

How to Study a Word

LOOK at the word.
SAY the word.
THINK about the word.
WRITE the word.
CHECK the spelling.

1 **Short Vowel Patterns**

A short vowel sound is usually spelled *a, e, i, o,* or *u* and is followed by a consonant sound.

ask	**lock**
next	shut
mix	

2 **Long Vowel Sounds**

The long *a* sound can be spelled with the pattern *a*-consonant-*e, ai,* or *ay.*

sh**ade**	pl**ay**
t**ai**l	

The long *e* sound is often spelled with the pattern *e*-consonant-*e, ea,* or *ee.*

th**ese**	d**ee**p
b**ea**ch	

The long *i* sound can be spelled with the pattern *i*-consonant-*e, igh,* or *ie.*

r**ipe**	t**ie**
r**igh**t	

The long *o* sound can be spelled with the pattern *o*-consonant-*e, oa,* or *ow.*

h**ome**	**ow**n
s**oa**p	

The long *u* sound /yo͞o/ or /o͞o/ may be spelled with the pattern *u*-consonant-*e, ew,* or *oo.*

use	b**oo**th
dr**ew**	

The long *i* sound at the end of a word may be spelled *y.*

cr**y**

The long *e* sound at the end of a word may be spelled *y.*

penn**y**

3 **Other Vowel Sounds**

The vowel sound in *cook* may be spelled with the pattern *oo* or *u.*

w**oo**ds	p**u**ll

The sound /ou/ is often spelled with the pattern *ow* or *ou.*

t**ow**n	pr**ou**d

The sound /oi/ is spelled with the pattern *oi* or *oy.*

n**oi**se	b**oy**

The vowel sound in *saw* can be spelled with the pattern *aw, a* before *l, ough,* or *augh.*

s**aw**	th**ough**t
t**a**lk	c**augh**t

4 **Vowel + *r* Sounds**

The vowel + *r* sounds you hear in *dark* can be spelled with the pattern *ar.*

st**ar**t

The vowel + *r* sounds you hear in *near* can be spelled with the pattern *ear.*

y**ear**

The vowel + *r* sounds you hear in *more* can be spelled with the patterns *or* and *ore.*

st**or**y	st**ore**

The vowel + *r* sounds in *first* can be spelled with the pattern *er, ir, ur,* or *or.*

w**er**e	t**ur**n
f**ir**st	w**or**k

5 Consonant Sounds

The /s/ sound you hear at the beginning of *city* may be spelled *c* when the *c* is followed by *i* or *e*.

circle   on**ce**

The /j/ sound you hear at the beginning of *just* can be spelled with the consonant *j* or with the consonant *g* followed by *e*.

just   lar**ge**

6 Syllable Patterns

The schwa + *r* sounds that you hear in *grandmother* are often spelled with the pattern *er*.

nev**er**

The schwa + *l* sounds that you hear in *people* can be spelled with the pattern *le*.

tab**le**

Some two-syllable words have the vowel-consonant-consonant-vowel pattern (VCCV). Divide a word with this pattern between the two consonants to find the syllables. Look for spelling patterns you have learned. Spell the word by syllables.

win/ dow   din/ ner

7 Word Endings

Add *s* to most words to name more than one. Add *es* to words that end with *s*, *x*, *sh*, or *ch* to name more than one.

trips   wish**es**
bus**es**   peach**es**
box**es**

If a base word ends with *e*, drop the *e* before adding the ending *-ed* or *-ing*.

shap**e** - shap**ed**
tak**e** - tak**ing**

If a base word ends with a vowel and a single consonant, double the consonant before adding *-ed* or *-ing*.

drop**ped**   hit**ting**

When a base word ends with a consonant and *y*, change the *y* to *i* before adding *-es* or *-ed*.

sky - sk**ies**
try - tr**ied**

8 Prefixes and Suffixes

Prefixes are added to the beginning of base words or word roots. *Re-*, *un-*, and *dis-* are prefixes.

reread   **dis**like
unfair

Suffixes are added to the end of base words or word roots. These word parts are suffixes: *-ful*, *-ly*, *-er*.

play**ful**   writ**er**
soft**ly**

9 Homophones and Contractions See Problem Words, p. 160.

A Resource for Grammar, Usage, Punctuation, and Capitalization

SENTENCES

Definition

A **sentence** is a group of words that tells a complete thought. It tells who or what, and it tells what happens. A sentence begins with a capital letter.

> **L**ightning flashed in the sky.　　**T**he forest ranger spotted fire.

- A group of words is not a sentence unless it has both parts—the part that tells who or what and the part that tells what happens. These examples are NOT sentences.

> Flashed in the sky.　　During the storm.　　When the tree fell.

Kinds of Sentences

There are four kinds of sentences.

- A **statement** is a sentence that tells something. It ends with a period.

> Deserts are dry**.**

- A **question** is a sentence that asks something. It ends with a question mark.

> Do you like deserts**?**

- A **command** is a sentence that tells someone to do something. It ends with a period.

> Always carry water**.**

- An **exclamation** shows strong feeling. It ends with an exclamation point (**!**).

> How hot it was**!**　　　　It was so hot**!**

Subjects and Predicates

Every sentence has a **subject** and a **predicate.**

- The **subject** tells whom or what the sentence is about.

> **Captain Ortega** is a good pilot.　**The large jet** carries many people.

- The **predicate** is the part of a sentence that tells what the subject does or is.

> Captain Ortega **is a good pilot.**　The large jet **carries many people.**

Run-on Sentences

A **run-on sentence** is two or more sentences that are run together incorrectly. Do not run sentences together.

- Correct a run-on sentence by adding end marks and capital letters to separate each complete thought.

Run-on: Electricians often wear rubber gloves electricity cannot go through rubber.

Corrected: Electricians often wear rubber gloves. **E**lectricity cannot go through rubber.

NOUNS

Definition

A **noun** names a person, a place, or a thing.

Nouns		
Persons	boy student	writer Li Chen
Places	lake Fenway Park	Olympia mountain
Things	boat calendar	sweater *Little Women*

Common and Proper Nouns

A **common noun** names any person, place, or thing.

    doctor   country   holiday

A **proper noun** names a particular person, place, or thing. Proper nouns begin with capital letters. A proper noun, like *Pine Lake*, may have more than one word. Begin each important word in a proper noun with a capital letter.

    Dr. Juarez   Sudan   Fourth of July

Common Nouns	Proper Nouns
My **friend** swam today. Her **dog** went with her. The **lake** was cold.	**Suzy** swam today. **Buddy** went with her. **Pine Lake** was cold.

Singular and Plural Nouns

Singular nouns name one person, place, or thing.

Julie climbed a <u>tree</u>.   She played on a <u>swing</u>.

Plural nouns name more than one person, place, or thing.

Julie climbed two <u>trees</u>.   She played on some <u>swings</u>.

- Form the plural of most nouns by adding *s* or *es* to the singular. Look at the ending of the singular noun to help you decide on whether to add *s* or *es* to form the plural.

Rules for Forming Plural Nouns

1.	Most singular nouns: Add *s*	street house	street**s** house**s**
2.	Nouns ending in *s*, *sh*, *ch*, or *x*: Add *es*.	dress dish bench ax	dress**es** dish**es** bench**es** ax**es**
3.	Nouns ending with a consonant and *y*: Change the *y* to *i* and add *es*.	city cranberry	cit**ies** cranber**ries**
4.	Nouns that have special plural spelling.	woman mouse foot ox	wom**en** m**ice** f**eet** ox**en**

Singular and Plural Possessive Nouns

A **possessive noun** shows ownership. Possessive nouns can be singular or plural. When a possessive noun is singular, it shows that one person, place, or thing has or owns something.

- To form the possessive of a singular noun, add an apostrophe (') and *s*.

Singular Nouns	Singular Possessive Nouns
boy	boy**'s** bike
Amy	Amy**'s** game
cat	cat**'s** paws

When a possessive noun is plural, it shows that more than one person, place, or thing has or owns something.

- If a plural noun ends with *s,* add only an apostrophe.

Plural Nouns	Plural Possessive Nouns
teams	two teams**'** bats
bunnies	bunnies**'** carrots
classes	classes**'** books

VERBS

Definition

A **verb** is a word that shows action. The verb is the main word in the predicate.

The fire **burns** brightly. It **lasts** for hours.

Helping Verbs

Has and *have* are **helping verbs.** They help other verbs to show past time.

*   Use *has* with a singular noun in the subject and with *he, she,* or *it.*

    Ada **has** played the game.   She **has** enjoyed it.

*   Use *have* with a plural noun in the subject and with *I, you, we,* or *they.*

    The boys **have** helped her.   I **have** watched.

The Verb *be*

The verb *be* does not show action. It tells what someone or something is or was.

*   The verb *be* has special forms.

    I **am** in fifth grade.   I **was** late for school today.

    You **are** younger.   The other students **were** already inside.

    Mr. Roberts **is** my teacher.

*   *Am, is,* and *are* show present time.

    I **am** sleepy now.   Today we **are** in Maine.

    It **is** a four-hour drive.

*   *Was* and *were* show past time.

    It **was** a long trip.   Friday we **were** in Vermont.

Subject	Present	Past
I	am	was
you	are	were
he, she, it	is	was
singular noun (John)	is	was
we	are	were
they	are	were
plural noun (dogs)	are	were

Verbs in the Present

Verbs show action in sentences. Verbs also tell when the action happens.

A **verb in present time** tells what is happening now. The form of a verb in present time depends on its subject.

- Add *s* to a verb in the present when the noun in the subject is singular.

  The **dog** barks at the snowman.   **Jill** laughs.

- Do not add *s* to a verb in the present when the noun in the subject is plural.

  The boys **shovel**.   Their parents **start** the car.

- Add *es* to a verb that ends with *s, sh, ch,* or *x* when it is used with a singular noun.

  The **broom** brushes the snow off the porch.

- If a verb ends with a consonant and *y,* change the *y* to *i* before adding *es.*

  A neighbor carries the shovel to the car.

Singular	Plural
Rob **tosses** a ball.	The boys **toss** the ball.
My grandfather **fishes**.	The girls **fish**.
Mother **watches** us.	Friends **mix** the salad.
Emily **mixes** the salad.	People **watch** us.

Verbs in the Past

A **verb in past time** shows that an action has already happened.

- Add *-ed* to most verbs to show past time.

    We **cooked** our dinner over a campfire.   It **begged** for a peanut.

    A squirrel **hoped** for a few crumbs.   Then the squirrel **hurried** away.

The spelling of some verbs changes when you add *-ed*.

- When a verb ends in *e*, drop the *e* before adding *-ed*.

    rac**e** - **e** + **ed** + rac**ed**   jok**e** - **e** + **ed** = jok**ed**

- When a verb ends with a consonant and *y*, change the *y* to *i* and add *-ed*.

    stud**y** - **y** + **i** + **ed** = stud**ied**   hurr**y** - **y** + **i** + **ed** = hurr**ied**

- When a verb ends with one vowel followed by one consonant, double the final consonant and add *-ed*.

    sto**p** + **p** + **ed** = sto**pped**   hu**g** + **g** + **ed** = hu**gged**

    pla**n** + **n** + **ed** = pla**nned**   dra**g** + **g** + **ed** = dra**gged**

Irregular Verbs

Some verbs are special: they do not end in *-ed* to show past time. They have one spelling to show past time and another spelling when used with *has, have,* or *had.*

    Present: Many people **run** in Boston's big race.

        Past: William **ran** in the race last year.

  With *has*: Anita **has run** in the race many times.

There are many irregular verbs in the English language. See the chart on the next page.

Irregular Verbs

Present	Past	Past with *has, have,* or *had*
begin	began	(has, have, had) begun
blow	blew	(has, have, had) blown
break	broke	(has, have, had) broken
bring	brought	(has, have, had) brought
choose	chose	(has, have, had) chosen
come	came	(has, have, had) come
do	did	(has, have, had) done
eat	ate	(has, have, had) eaten
fly	flew	(has, have, had) flown
freeze	froze	(has, have, had) frozen
give	gave	(has, have, had) given
go	went	(has, have, had) gone
grow	grew	(has, have, had) grown
know	knew	(has, have, had) known
make	made	(has, have, had) made
ring	rang	(has, have, had) rung
run	ran	(has, have, had) run
say	said	(has, have, had) said
see	saw	(has, have, had) seen
sing	sang	(has, have, had) sung
speak	spoke	(has, have, had) spoken
steal	stole	(has, have, had) stolen
swim	swam	(has, have, had) swum
take	took	(has, have, had) taken
tear	tore	(has, have, had) torn
think	thought	(has, have, had) thought
wear	wore	(has, have, had) worn
write	wrote	(has, have, had) written

ADJECTIVES

What Are Adjectives?

An **adjective** is a word that describes a noun.

- An adjective may tell *what kind.*

    Loud sirens woke me up. (What kind of sirens?)

    The **old** barn was on fire. (What kind of barn?)

- Adjectives such as *one, ten, many,* and *several* tell *how many.*

    Two families were rescued by firefighters.

    Fire trucks from **many** towns arrived.

- Adjectives usually come before the noun they are describing.

    A **black** dog barked at the trucks.
    Firefighters sprayed water on the **angry** flames.

Articles

A, an, and *the* are special adjectives called **articles**. *A* and *an* refer to any person, place, or thing. *The* refers to a particular person, place, or thing.

- Use *a* and *an* before singular nouns.
- Use *the* before singular and plural nouns.

a	Use before a word that begins with a consonant sound.	**a** jet **a** high step
an	Use before a word that begins with a vowel sound.	**an** engineer **an** hour
the	Use before singular and plural words.	**the** plans

Comparing with Adjectives

To compare two people, places, or things, add *-er* to most adjectives.

> Mars is a **smaller** planet than Jupiter.

To compare more than two people, places, or things, add *-est*.

> Pluto is the **smallest** planet of all.

Adjective	Compare two.	Compare three or more.
Neptune is **warm**.	Uranus is **warmer** than Neptune.	Saturn is the **warmest** of the three.

ADVERBS

What Are Adverbs?

A word that describes a verb is an **adverb**.

- Adverbs tell *how, when*, and *where* an action happens.

> Kim walked up to the horse **bravely**. (walked how?)

> **Next**, she sat on the horse. (sat when?)

> The horse stood **there**. (stood where?)

- Adverbs that tell *how* usually end in *-ly*.

How		When		Where	
easily	safely	always	soon	ahead	here
certainly	secretly	first	then	around	nearby
fast	slowly	later	today	away	out
happily	softly	next	tomorrow	everywhere	there
quietly	together	often	yesterday	far	upstairs

PRONOUNS

Definition

A **pronoun** takes the place of one or more nouns.

Nouns	Pronouns
<u>Carl</u> watches the swimmers. <u>The swimmers</u> listen for the whistle.	**He** watches the swimmers. **They** listen for the whistle.

Subject Pronouns

The pronouns *I, you, he, she, it, we,* and *they* are **subject pronouns**. Pronouns can be singular or plural.

Subject Pronouns	
Singular	**Plural**
I you he, she, it	we you they

- Use **subject pronouns** as subjects of sentences.

    I will compete in a swimming race.   **You** offered some tips.

Use the form of the verb in the present that goes with the subject pronoun.

- Add *s* or *es* to a verb in the present when the subject is *he, she,* or *it*.

    She **fixes** dinner.   He **sets** the table.

- Do not add *s* or *es* to a verb in the present when the subject is *I, you, we,* or *they*.

    I **fix** dinner.   We **set** the table.

Object Pronouns

The pronouns *me, you, him, her, it, us,* and *them* are **object pronouns**.

• Object pronouns follow action verbs and words like *to, for, at, of,* and *with*.

Nouns	Pronouns
Nina painted with <u>Lou</u>.	Nina painted with **him**.
Ben and I met <u>Nina and Lou</u>.	Ben and I met **them**.
Ben brought <u>a brush</u>.	Ben brought **it**.

• Object pronouns can be singular or plural.

Object Pronouns	
Singular	**Plural**
me	us
you	you
him, her, it	them

• Use **object pronouns** as objects of sentences.

Mr. Russell told **us** about the play.   Dale and Kristin made a costume for **you**.

Lisa tried out for **it.**   Joy watched **them** last night.

• *It* and *you* are both subject or object pronouns.

Subject Pronouns	Object Pronouns
It was a big success.	The parents loved **it**.
You came backstage.	The flowers are for **you**.

I and *me*

- Use *I* as the subject of a sentence. Use *me* as an object pronoun. Always capitalize the word *I*.

    Subject Pronoun: **I** left a message for Nat.
    Object Pronoun: Nat called **me** right back.

- Name yourself last when you talk about another person and yourself.

    Nat and I helped Mom.   She gave **Nat and me** some money.

- Try this test if you have trouble choosing between *I* and *me*. Say the sentence with only *I* or *me*. Leave out the other noun.

    Nat and I went to the store.   **I** went to the store.
    Dad walked with **Nat and me**.   Dad walked with **me**.

Possessive Pronouns

A **possessive pronoun** shows ownership. Possessive pronouns can take the place of possessive nouns.

Possessive Nouns	Possessive Pronouns
<u>Amy's</u> radio is broken. She took it to <u>Al's</u> shop. Amy has <u>the twins'</u> radio.	**Her** radio is broken. She took it to **his** shop. Amy has **their** radio.

The pronouns *my, your, her, his, its, our,* and *their* are possessive pronouns.

My class watches the gorillas.   **Her** best friend is Michael.
Their names are Koko and Michael.   Michael paints a picture on **his** paper.
Koko wants to shake **your** hand.   The gorilla sits on **its** blanket.
Michael waves to **our** teacher.

ABBREVIATIONS

Abbreviations are shortened forms of words. Most abbreviations begin with a capital letter and end with a period.

- **Titles**

Mr. *(Mister)* Mr. Pedro Arupe	Sr. *(Senior)* James Morton, Sr.
Mrs. *(Mistress)* Mrs. Jane Chang	Jr. *(Junior)* James Morton, Jr.
Ms. Carla Tower	Dr. *(Doctor)* Dr. Ellen Masters

  Note: *Miss* is not an abbreviation and does not end with a period.

- **Words used in addresses**

St. *(Street)*	Blvd. *(Boulevard)*
Rd. *(Road)*	Ave. *(Avenue)*

- **Days of the week**

Sun. *(Sunday)*	Wed. *(Wednesday)*	Fri. *(Friday)*
Mon. *(Monday)*	Thurs. *(Thursday)*	Sat. *(Saturday)*
Tues. *(Tuesday)*		

- **Months of the year**

Jan. *(January)*	Apr. *(April)*	Oct. *(October)*
Feb. *(February)*	Aug. *(August)*	Nov. *(November)*
Mar. *(March)*	Sept. *(September)*	Dec. *(December)*

  Note: May, June, and July are not abbreviated.

ABBREVIATIONS (continued)

- **States**

The United States Postal Service uses two capital letters and no period in each of its state abbreviations.

AL *(Alabama)*	LA *(Louisiana)*	OH *(Ohio)*
AK *(Alaska)*	ME *(Maine)*	OK *(Oklahoma)*
AZ *(Arizona)*	MD *(Maryland)*	OR *(Oregon)*
AR *(Arkansas)*	MA *(Massachusetts)*	PA *(Pennsylvania)*
CA *(California)*	MI *(Michigan)*	RI *(Rhode Island)*
CO *(Colorado)*	MN *(Minnesota)*	SC *(South Carolina)*
CT *(Connecticut)*	MS *(Mississippi)*	SD *(South Dakota)*
DE *(Delaware)*	MO *(Missouri)*	TN *(Tennessee)*
FL *(Florida)*	MT *(Montana)*	TX *(Texas)*
GA *(Georgia)*	NE *(Nebraska)*	UT *(Utah)*
HI *(Hawaii)*	NV *(Nevada)*	VT *(Vermont)*
ID *(Idaho)*	NH *(New Hampshire)*	VA *(Virginia)*
IL *(Illinois)*	NJ *(New Jersey)*	WA *(Washington)*
IN *(Indiana)*	NM *(New Mexico)*	WV *(West Virginia)*
IA *(Iowa)*	NY *(New York)*	WI *(Wisconsin)*
KS *(Kansas)*	NC *(North Carolina)*	WY *(Wyoming)*
KY *(Kentucky)*	ND *(North Dakota)*	

TITLES

Underlining

Titles of books, newspapers, magazines, and TV series are underlined. The important words and the first and last words are capitalized.

<u>The Call of the Wild</u>   <u>Time</u>   <u>Nature</u>

Computer Tip: Use italic type for the titles of books and newspapers instead of underlining: *Life on the Mississippi; The New York Times.*

Quotation marks

Put quotation marks *(" ")* around the titles of short stories, articles, songs, poems, and book chapters.

"The Red Pony" (short story)   "Song of the South" (song)

QUOTATIONS

Quotation marks

A **direct quotation** tells a speaker's exact words. Use quotation marks *(" ")* to set off a direct quotation from the rest of the sentence.

"Please iron your shirt tonight," said Ms. Hilton.

Begin a quotation with a capital letter. When a quotation comes at the end of a sentence, use a comma to separate the quotation from the words that tell who is speaking. Put end marks inside the last quotation mark.

The principal announced, "The library will be open today."

Writing a conversation

Begin a new paragraph each time a new person begins speaking.

"Are you going to drive all the way to Columbus in one day?" asked my Uncle Ben.

"I really haven't decided," said my father. "I was hoping that you would share the driving with me."

CAPITALIZATION

Rules for capitalization

Every sentence begins with a capital letter.

> <u>W</u>hat a wonderful day this is!

The pronoun *I* is always a capital letter.

> What can <u>I</u> do this afternoon?

Begin each important word in the names of particular persons, pets, places, and things (proper nouns) with a capital letter.

> <u>M</u>orris   <u>G</u>ulf of <u>M</u>exico   <u>A</u>very <u>P</u>lace   <u>W</u>ashington <u>M</u>onument

Titles and their abbreviations when used with a person's name begin with a capital letter. Use a capital letter for a person's initials.

> <u>S</u>heriff Tilden   <u>M</u>rs. Garcia   Laura <u>B</u>. Hecht   Judge Diego

Family titles when they are used as names or as parts of names begin with a capital letter.

> We called <u>A</u>unt Leslie.   May we leave now, <u>G</u>randpa?

Begin the names of days, months, and holidays with a capital letter.

> Next <u>M</u>onday is the <u>F</u>ourth of <u>J</u>uly.

The names of groups begin with a capital letter.

> <u>A</u>spen <u>M</u>ountain <u>C</u>lub   <u>I</u>nternational <u>L</u>eague

The first and last words and all important words in the titles of books and newspapers begin with a capital letter. Titles of books and newspapers are underlined.

> <u>Secrets of a Wildlife Watcher</u>   <u>The Los Angeles Times</u>

CAPITALIZATION (continued)

The first word in the greeting and the closing of a letter begins with a capital letter.

<u>D</u>ear Melissa,   <u>S</u>incerely yours,

PUNCTUATION

End marks

There are three end marks. A period *(.)* ends a statement or a command. A question mark *(?)* follows a question. An exclamation point *(!)* follows an exclamation.

The notebook is on the shelf<u>.</u> *(statement)*
Watch that program at eight tonight<u>.</u> *(command)*
Where does the trail end<u>?</u> *(question)*
This is your highest score this year<u>!</u> *(exclamation)*

Apostrophe

Add an apostrophe *(')* and *s* to a singular noun to make it show ownership.

day<u>'s</u>   James<u>'s</u>   grandfather<u>'s</u>   community<u>'s</u>

For a plural noun ending in *s*, add just an apostrophe *(')* to show ownership.

sisters<u>'</u>   families<u>'</u>   Smiths<u>'</u>   hound dogs<u>'</u>

For a plural noun that does not end in *s*, add an apostrophe *(')* and *s*.

teeth<u>'s</u>   men<u>'s</u>   children<u>'s</u>

Use an apostrophe in contractions in place of missing letters.

isn<u>'</u>t *(is not)*	it<u>'</u>s *(it is)*
can<u>'</u>t *(cannot)*	I<u>'</u>m *(I am)*
won<u>'</u>t *(will not)*	they<u>'</u>ve *(they have)*
wasn<u>'</u>t *(was not)*	they<u>'</u>ll *(they will)*
we<u>'</u>re *(we are)*	

Comma

A comma (,) tells the reader to pause between the words that it separates.

Use commas to separate a series of three or more words. Put a comma after each item in the series except the last one.

> We made a salad of lettuce, peppers, and onions.

You can combine two short, related sentences to make one compound sentence. Use a comma and the connecting word *and, but,* or *or.*

> The sky became dark, and we heard thunder.

Use commas after *yes, no, well,* and order words when they begin a sentence.

> Yes, it's a perfect day for a picnic.   Well, I'll make dessert.
> First, find the basket.   No, the ants will not bother us.

Use a comma or commas to set off the names of people who are spoken to directly.

> Gloria, hold this light for me.   How was the movie, Grandma?

Use a comma to separate the month and the day from the year.

> I was born on July 3, 1988.

Use a comma between the names of a city and a state.

> Denver, Colorado   Tulsa, Oklahoma

Use a comma after the greeting in a friendly letter.

> Dear Tayo,   Dear Aunt Claudia,

Use a comma after the closing in a letter.

> Your friend,   Yours truly,

Quotation Marks

See Quotations, p. 156.

GRAMMAR GUIDE

PROBLEM WORDS

Words	Rules	Examples
are our	*Are* is a verb. *Our* is a possessive pronoun.	<u>Are</u> these gloves yours? This is <u>our</u> car.
doesn't don't	Use *doesn't* with singular nouns, *he*, *she*, and *it*. Use *don't* with plural nouns, *I*, *you*, *we*, and *they*.	Dad <u>doesn't</u> swim. We <u>don't</u> swim.
good well	Use the adjective *good* to describe nouns. Use the adverb *well* to describes verbs.	The weather looks <u>good</u>. She sings <u>well</u>.
its it's	*Its* is a possessive pronoun. *It's* means "it is" (contraction).	The dog wagged <u>its</u> tail. <u>It's</u> cold today.
let leave	*Let* means "to allow." *Leave* means "to go away from" or "to lct stay."	Please <u>let</u> me go swimming. I will <u>leave</u> soon. <u>Leave</u> it on my desk.
set sit	*Set* means "to put." *Sit* means "to rest or stay in one place."	<u>Set</u> the vase on the table. Please <u>sit</u> in this chair.
their there they're	*Their* means "belonging to them." *There* means "at or in that place." *They're* means "they are" (contraction).	<u>Their</u> coats are on the bed. Is Carlos <u>there</u>? <u>They're</u> going to the store.
two to too	*Two* is a number. *To* means "toward." *Too* means "also" or "more than enough."	I bought <u>two</u> shirts. A cat ran <u>to</u> the tree. Can we go <u>too</u>? I ate <u>too</u> many peas.
your you're	*Your* is a possessive pronoun. *You're* means "you are" (contraction).	Are these <u>your</u> glasses? <u>You're</u> late again!

ADVERB USAGE

Negatives

A negative word or negative contraction says "no" or "not." Do not use two negatives to express one negative idea.

> Incorrect: We can't do nothing.
>
> Correct: We <u>can't</u> do <u>anything</u>.
>
> Correct: We <u>can</u> do <u>nothing</u>.

Negative Words

no	nobody	nothing
never	none	nowhere
neither	no one	

PRONOUN USAGE

I and me

Use *I* as the subject of a sentence. Use *me* as an object pronoun and after words such as *to, with, for,* and *at.* Name yourself last when you talk about another person and yourself.

> <u>Beth and I</u> are leaving for the beach. He will meet <u>me</u>.
>
> <u>Kwesi and I</u> will practice. Give the directions to <u>Roy and me</u>.

MY NOTES

_____

_____

_____

_____

_____

_____

_____

_____

_____

_____

_____

_____

_____

Ask yourself each question. Check your paper for mistakes. Correct any mistakes you find. Put a check in the box when you find no more mistakes.

☐ **1.** Did I indent each paragraph?

☐ **2.** Does each sentence tell one complete thought?

☐ **3.** Did I end each sentence with the correct mark?

☐ **4.** Did I begin each sentence with a capital letter?

☐ **5.** Did I use capital letters correctly in other places?

☐ **6.** Did I use commas correctly?

☐ **7.** Did I spell all the words the right way?

Is there anything else you should look for? Make your own proofreading list.

☐ _____

☐ _____

☐ _____

☐ _____

☐ _____

☐ _____

☐ _____

☐ _____

☐ _____

☐ _____

☐ _____

PROOFREADING MARKS

Mark	Explanation	Example
¶	Begin a new paragraph. Indent the paragraph.	¶ We went to an air show last Saturday. Eight jets flew across the sky in the shape of V's, X's, and diamonds.
∧	Add letters, words, or sentences.	The leaves were red ∧ orange. *(and)*
℘	Take out words, sentences, and punctuation marks. Correct spelling.	The sky is bright blew. *(blue)* Huge clouds move quickly.
/	Change a capital letter to a small letter.	The Fireflies blinked in the dark.
≡	Change a small letter to a capital letter.	New York city is exciting.